CARE OF THE HORSE
AT GRASS

CARE OF THE HORSE AT GRASS

Zoe Davies

B.T. Batsford Ltd · London

Typeset by Servis Filmsetting Ltd,
Manchester

and printed in Great Britain by
The Bath Press, Lower Bristol Road, Avon

Published by
B.T. Batsford Ltd
4 Fitzhardinge Street
London W1H 0AH

A catalogue record for this book is available
from the British Library

ISBN 0 7134 7570 6

Disclaimer of Liability

The Author and Publisher shall have neither
liability nor responsibility to any person or
entity with respect to any loss or damage
caused or alleged to be caused directly or
indirectly by the information contained in
this book. While the book is as accurate as
the Author can make it, there may be errors,
omissions, and inaccuracies.

   The Publisher would also like to make
clear that where the horse is referred to as
'he' or 'him', this is for the sake of clarity
and consistency and is intended to cover all
horses, mares included.

CONTENTS

Acknowledgements

Special thanks should be given to my husband Ian and daughters Sophie and Katie, who allowed me the time and encouraged me to sit down and write this book in peace (most of the time!).

Thanks are also due to Shirley O'Cleirigh, who read through and commented on the original draft, and Jane Royston, my editor at Batsford. Particular thanks also to Joanna Prestwich, who provided the photographs after many delays due to the weather! Thanks to Tim Brazil MRCVS of Liverpool University Veterinary School, for providing some of the more technical photographs.

INTRODUCTION

Horses are grazing animals. This is how they have evolved over millions of years, wandering in herds across vast areas of land in search of nourishment. As the horse became domesticated his access to land became restricted to smaller areas, such as paddocks or corrals.

Whether horses are turned out for a couple of hours, or live out permanently, there is no doubt that their health and well-being will benefit as a result. This is after all their 'natural' environment, or as close to it as they can get. Psychologically speaking, horses are happier if they have company and access to good safe grazing and water. All horses need to be turned out on a regular basis but special attention must be given to their care. Problems can occur, not just in freezing conditions but on glorious summer days.

This book aims to provide a sound knowledge of the management of horses which spend any time at grass. It will point out aspects of management which are often overlooked, sometimes with serious consequences.

If the horse and his environment are cared for properly then he will be happier, healthier and less prone to stress and disease **(1)**.

1 Young foals need plenty of space to play in safety

Equine evolution

From the study of fossils we have been able to deduce that the horse first appeared on earth as long ago as 55 million years. The earliest ancestors were mammals known as *condylarthra*. These had five toes on each limb and were the forebears of all hoofed mammals.

The horse belongs to the family *Equidae*, the first animal from this evolutionary course being *eohippus* (scientific name *hyracotherium*). He appeared during the Eocene period and is also known as the 'dawn horse'. Small and fox-like in appearance, he had an arched back, four horn-covered toes on his forefeet and three on his hindfeet. All the toes were padded. *Eohippus'* brain was small and he used his 44 teeth to browse, choosing shrubs as his main diet. (**Fig. 1** shows the evolutionary pathway through the different periods.)

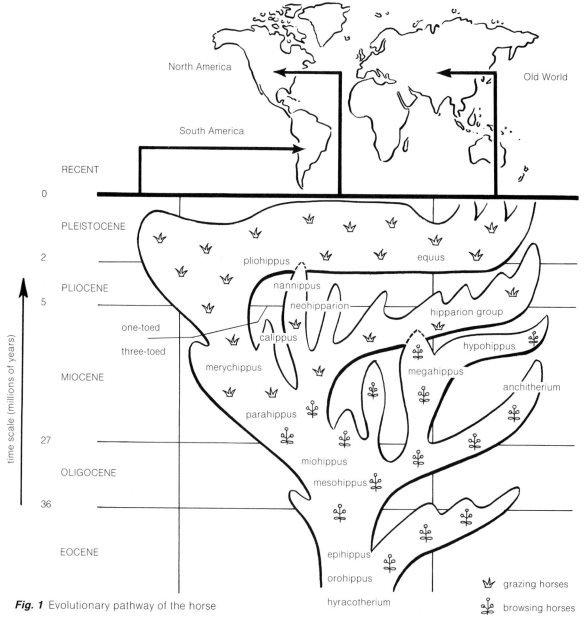

Fig. 1 Evolutionary pathway of the horse

4 toes

3 toes

1 toe

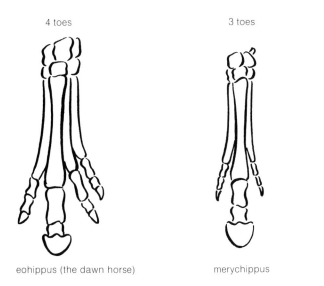

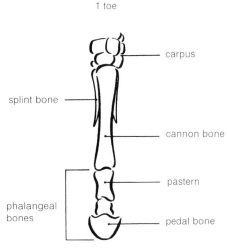

carpus

splint bone

cannon bone

pastern

phalangeal
bones

pedal bone

eohippus (the dawn horse)

merychippus

equus (present day horse)

Fig. 2 Evolutionary changes in the forelimb of the horse

Subtle genetic changes over long periods of time are inevitable and, in this instance, as the climate changed and the swamps dried out, providing firmer ground, the four toes became obsolete. Over millions of years the number of toes were gradually reduced to help the animal move faster over the plains until the first 'one-toed' ancestor of the horse came into being, some 10 million years ago. This was *pliohippus*. The ancestors of *pliohippus* did not simply 'lose' toes, but because they were no longer used they shrank in size, becoming tiny dew hooves (similar to the dew claws of a dog). The chestnut present on the inside of the horse's leg just above the knee is the remains of the first toe lost during evolution and the ergots on the back of the fetlock joints are small pieces of horn, remnants of the second and fourth toes **(Fig. 2)**.

The small thin splint bones are the remains of the second metacarpal (foreleg) and metatarsal (hindleg) bones. A steady increase in body size and length of the limbs was accompanied by substantial changes in the teeth. From being fairly soft and short crowned (ideally suited to a diet of swamp plants), they became longer crowned, with ridged grinding surfaces enabling them to cope with the tougher grass plants. The skull also had to increase in size to accommodate these longer teeth.

All domestic horses are members of the species *Equus caballus* and are descended from the wild horses that roamed the plains of central Asia. These survive today as the Mongolian wild horses (Przewalski's horse). They are very few in number and live mostly in zoos. There has been a recent attempt to introduce a herd back into the wild, and this has so far been successful.

Other equine species alive today are the common zebra, African wild ass, Grevy's zebra and the Asiatic wild ass (onager). These can all interbreed, although some of the resultant offspring are infertile, such as the mule; this is because some of the different species have differing numbers of chromosomes. Crossing Przewalski's horse with domestic horses, however, results in fertile offspring even though the former has two fewer chromosomes. The modern-day horse has now evolved into a free-ranging, grazing animal. It has developed a unique digestive system to cope with its diet; this will be discussed later.

Part 1
MANAGEMENT OF THE HORSE OUTDOORS

1
SENSES, BEHAVIOUR AND PRACTICAL CARE

Senses

Sight

Horses have remarkable all-round vision. Their eyes are set high up on the head towards the side rather than at the front **(Fig. 3)**, and they have the ability to see predators whilst they have their heads down grazing. The horse's eye is huge, one of the biggest in the animal kingdom, larger even than that of the elephant or whale. It possesses a light-intensifying device called the *tapetum lucidum*, a layer in the eye which reflects light back onto the retina, enabling the horse to see in dim light; it also glows in the dark (similar to cat's eyes). These indicate that the horse is

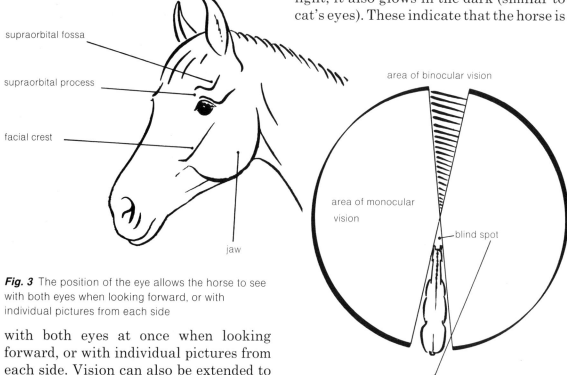

supraorbital fossa

supraorbital process

facial crest

jaw

Fig. 3 The position of the eye allows the horse to see with both eyes when looking forward, or with individual pictures from each side

area of binocular vision

area of monocular vision

blind spot

with both eyes at once when looking forward, or with individual pictures from each side. Vision can also be extended to the back simply by moving the head slightly **(Fig. 4)**, enabling them to see

Fig. 4 The horse's wide field of vision

probably nocturnal. He is most active at dawn and dusk.

Because the range of binocular vision is so limited, the horse has difficulty in judging distances. However, he is more sensitive to tiny movements at the edge of his range of vision. As you can see from **Fig. 4**, horses have two blind spots, just in front and immediately behind their body; thus the handler should be careful when approaching the horse from behind.

The eye lies in the orbit and is well protected by its position in the skull. Horses have excellent reflexes which also explains why injuries to the eye are so

rare. The basic anatomy of the eye is shown in **Fig. 5**. The eye works on the same principles as a camera, in that it inverts (turns upside down) images and projects them (in the eye) onto the retina. Rays of light enter the front of the eye and are bent by the cornea and lens **(Fig. 6)**. This bending of light focuses the object being viewed. The amount of light entering is regulated by the eyelid and the pupil. Once the light reaches the retina the image is transmitted via the optic nerve to the brain.

Horses were once thought to be colour blind like cattle and dogs. However, recent work has shown that they are more responsive to yellow, then green, then blue, and least of all red.

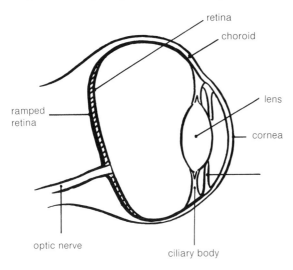

Fig. 5 A cross-section of the horse's eye, with 'ramped' retina to focus on food and predators simultaneously

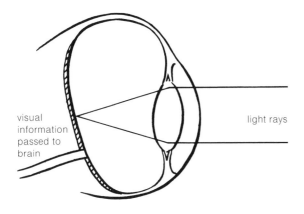

Fig. 6 The passage of light (images) into the horse's eye

Hearing

Horses have a highly developed sense of hearing and their sensitive ears can detect a wide range of sounds from very low to very high frequency. They can hear sounds well beyond the range of the human ear and as with humans, a horse's hearing begins to deteriorate with age.

The horse has large, mobile ears which can move independently of one another through a rotation of 360 degrees. This enables him to hear sounds from all directions without moving his body **(2)**.

The ear and its position are shown in **Fig. 7**. The horse has an unusual pouch attached to the eustachian tube known as the guttural pouch. This is exclusive to horses and donkeys (as well as a species of tree shrew). It consists of air sacs in close proximity to vital nerves and arteries. If the guttural pouch becomes infected it can be extremely serious if these vital structures are involved. Bleeding from the ear should always be taken seriously as it is usually caused by a fracture to the skull. However, this can sometimes be caused by a fungal infection of the guttural pouch.

2 Horses have a highly developed sense of hearing

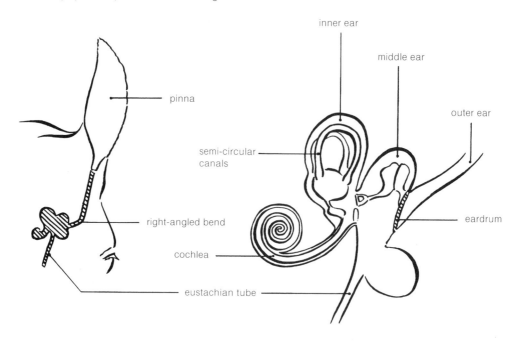

Fig. 7 Position and anatomy of the ear

Taste and smell

Horses have well developed senses of both taste and smell. In the wild, smell is an essential faculty in order to identify predators and to detect distant watering holes. Stallions need to smell when mares are coming into season (a stallion is able to smell a receptive mare from distances of up to half a mile) **(3)**.

Horses have huge heads, to house both their teeth and the specialized pits, called vomeronasal organs or Jacobsens organs. These pits are particularly effective at detecting scents or pheromones from other animals, enabling horses within a group to recognize one another. Each herd has its own identification system. When new horses are introduced they sniff each others nostrils, blowing air into the nasal cavities. This will be remembered. Mares employ their sense of smell to recognize their offspring.

Horses have the same four responses to taste as humans: bitter, sweet, sour and salt. However, they have a greater tolerance to bitter tastes than we do. Some

3 The 'Flehmen' posture of stallions

horses can be very fussy with regards to their feed. They are also able to distinguish between grasses and poisonous plants such as ragwort. They will, though, still eat this if they are very hungry. If ragwort is present in hay, it will lose its bitter taste and the horse will not be able to distinguish it.

Finally, it is a well-known fact that horses are able to 'smell' fear in a nervous rider.

Social behaviour

Horses are gregarious and social animals. In the case of wild horses, being social improves the individual's chance of survival **(4)**. Although the horse likes to be part of a social organization he usually shows some strong likes and dislikes for other horses in his company. The theory of a dominance hierarchy stems from work

4 Horses are social animals

done on animals which were competing for space, food or both. If none of these factors are restricted then horses do not usually form dominance hierarchies. In practice, though, most horses are restricted in the space they have to live in and do not have a choice as to their companions. It is unusual to find a naturally aggressive horse but they can be made so through incorrect training methods (often due to the total domination of the horse by the trainer).

In the wild, horses tend to form family groups whereby they spend most time with their mothers and siblings **(5)**. These relationships are normally long and stable, but with most domestic horses this situation is unlikely to exist as many groups tend to be split up for one reason or another.

5 Horses in a natural situation tend to form family groups whereby they spend most of their time with their mothers, brothers and sisters

If a group of domestic horses are able to form relationships over a period of time with no new horses being introduced then they will, like humans, form likes and dislikes of the other horses. Although the dominance hierarchy theory is debatable there is no doubt that some horses can be very aggressive to others and they can and do cause injuries. The bullied horse will suffer both mentally and physically and this situation should not be allowed to continue. The need for the company of other horses is instinctive and there is no doubt that horses which are turned out

with others whom they get on with are much happier than those who are turned out alone (6). One of the most endearing manifestations of social behaviour is the practice of 'grooming' each other (7).

The introduction of new horses to a group should be undertaken carefully. Simply turning them out together and hoping for the best is not worth the risk. Serious injuries may result if one or more of them become aggressive and chase the new arrivals. I have seen horses being chased over and through fences and gates when this has been done.

There are methods of introducing horses gradually. One of the most successful ways is to place the newcomer in a paddock or field next to the main group. They will then become familiar with each other over the fence (preferably a good strong fence or hedge so that they will not injure themselves if they strike out with their forelegs). They should be left like this for about a week, and then the new arrival should be turned out in the main field and introduced to each of the established group one at a time, making sure that they are settled. There is rarely a problem as they will already recognize the new horse. If grazing space is limited and fields have been divided into smaller paddocks for ease of management, then it is often a good idea to separate the geldings from the mares. This seems to reduce the incidence of aggression and therefore injury.

True and false rigs

Particularly in the summer months some geldings may cause problems when turned out with mares, and there is often a much

6 Horses must be able to get on with each other when they are turned out to graze

higher incidence of aggression, usually towards other geldings. Unfortunately, when colts/stallions are cut later than three years of age they have already begun their sexual behaviour patterns. If they have actually covered mares then castration does not always stop this sexual behaviour and they will carry on covering, or attempting to cover, after the operation. It is not unusual therefore to find geldings with strong sexual behaviour patterns and they can become a nuisance when turned out with mares, particularly when they come into season. Some geldings may even achieve full penetration of mares. Geldings which show this kind of behaviour may be defined as 'false rigs' (8).

The behaviour of false rigs varies from

7 Mutual grooming is an integral part of equine behaviour

true covering of mares to simply rounding them up. False rigs can be blood tested to see if they are a true rig, otherwise known as a cryptorchid. These horses have retained one or both testes (i.e. they have not dropped into the scrotal sac). The sperm produced by these undescended testes will be not be fertile, but the male hormones will still be produced and the horse will behave like a stallion. The only successful treatment is surgical removal

8 False rigs may chase other horses in their group and can become a real nuisance

of the single testis (unilateral cryptorchidism) or both testes (bilateral cryptorchidism). A blood test will determine the level of the male hormone testosterone. The results will show whether the horse is a true or false rig. Traditionally it was thought that false rigs had been 'cut proud', meaning that some testicular tissue had remained after castration. This has been scientifically discredited and there is absolutely no evidence to support this theory. There is no effective treatment for a false rig.

Practical care of horses

Catching and turning out

Horses can be temperamental and very strong creatures. Catching horses can be a nightmare for some horseowners. Certainly, rewarding a horse who is difficult to catch once he has been caught is effective, although it can be difficult for the handler to speak calmly and quietly to a horse he has just spent a great deal of time chasing about! Horses can sense this.

It is best to approach the horse from the left-hand side as this will be what he is used to. Do not approach from directly behind or in front. As the handler approaches he should stretch out his hand

for the horse to sniff; a small titbit such as a carrot may be useful at this stage. As the horse eats the titbit the rope of the head-collar can be quietly and gently placed around his neck **(9)**. This gives the handler some restraint whilst the headcollar is put on. Many people recommend that a bucket of feed will do the trick for particularly obstinate horses. This is fine if there is only one horse in the field, but it can create a dangerous situation with the

9 The rope can be placed around the horse's neck before the head collar is put on

handler in the middle of a group of fighting horses!

If all the horses are being brought in and stabled at night there is usually no problem as the difficult one will probably

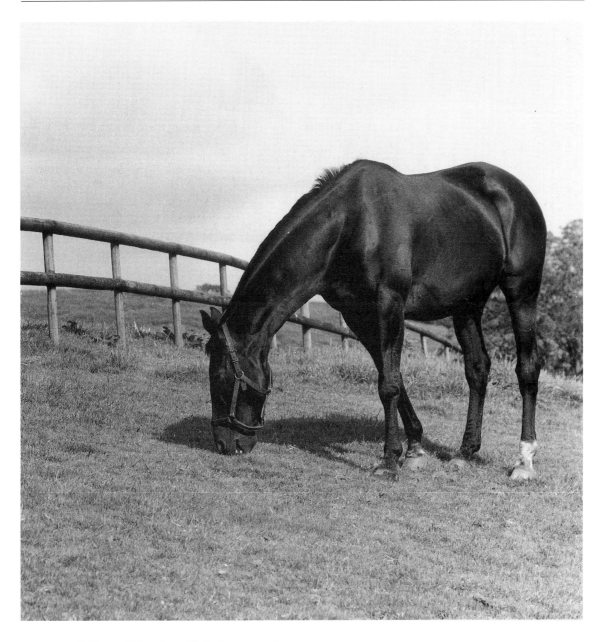

want to follow. If he is still being evasive try the food technique. In my experience it is normally the horses which are stabled for most of the time which are difficult to catch. Given more time out in the field grazing (instead of the odd hour here and there), they tend to become more amenable to being caught. Horses who are sometimes difficult to catch should always wear a headcollar as an aid to being caught **(10)**.

10 Horses who are difficult to catch should be turned out in a head collar

Horses need to be restrained whilst they are being led and should not be able to pull the handler in any direction they please. Some horses will require more restraint than others, depending on their age, temperament and previous education (or lack of it). The handler should start with the minimum amount of restraint and increase it as and when necessary.

Horses can become very strong when they are being turned out and in some cases the horse should be led out in a bridle to give the handler more control. If others are already present in the field they may come galloping over inquisitively. This can create difficulties when the horseowner is struggling with the gate at the same time. The handler should approach the gate with the horse facing the post. The horse can be held with one hand and the gate opened with the other. Once the gate is open the horse should be walked through and immediately turned round to face the gate which has been closed behind him. He can then be made to wait for a short time before the headcollar/halter and/or rope is gently removed. This will give the handler time to get out of the way should the horse decide to whisk round and gallop off. Galloping horses with trailing headcollars are all too common a sight, and a recipe for disaster.

The handler should always lead the horse from the side (not the front) as a frightened horse will simply run over the unfortunate handler.

Grooming

Grooming horses which are kept outdoors permanently should be restricted to the removal of mud, and keeping the mane and tail tidy and free from knots. Excessive grooming, particularly in the winter months, will strip the vital grease from the horse's coat thereby removing a layer of protection from the weather. However, certain areas need to be sponged clean including the eyes, nostrils, dock area and sheath on a regular basis. Separate sponges should be used for the head and rear end. The feet should also be attended to, being picked out to remove mud and stones.

Clipping and Trimming

Horses which are kept outdoors may still retain a smart appearance through trimming. The mane can be pulled but the tail is best left long as the horse turns its bottom towards the prevailing wind when the weather is particularly bad. It should, however, be kept at a reasonable length to prevent it being dragged through the mud, especially in the winter. Opinion varies as to whether the hair around the fetlock should be trimmed. Certainly in the winter months most horses benefit from the hair being left on, but those that are prone to greasy heels (see page 128) are better off having it removed. Excessive trimming of the ears (particularly the inside) is not recommended either, as flies can get inside, sometimes with serious consequences.

Horses can be clipped when they are kept outdoors if they are being regularly worked. Some horses grow thicker coats than others; the heavier types tending to grow heavier coats. If these horses are exercised they can sweat excessively and then take hours to dry. They should not be turned out in the winter whilst their coats are still wet as they may develop a chill. Suitable clips for such horses include a chest clip (where the hair is removed from under the neck to between the forelegs), and a low trace clip **(Fig. 8)**. Hunter and blanket clips remove too much of the horse's valuable protection. The clipped horse should be turned out in a New Zealand (weather proof) rug.

Rugs

Waterproof rugs are known as New Zealand rugs in Britain. There are several different designs and types and whichever is used, it must be fitted correctly so that it will right itself after the horse has rolled, and not cause discomfort **(11)**. When horses are clipped, or if the horse has a fine

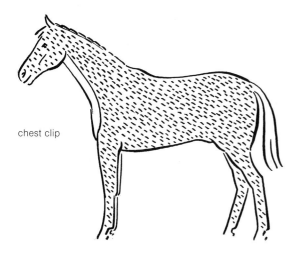

chest clip

Irish clip

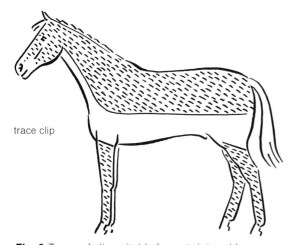

trace clip

Fig. 8 Types of clip suitable for outwintered horses (with rugs)

skin and/or coat, then a New Zealand rug is certainly good protection against bad weather. They are usually lined for extra warmth. Most rugs have leg straps which must also be fitted correctly, to prevent chaffing and rubbing **(12)**.

Head and neck hoods are often fitted to these rugs, some of which are made from stretch fabrics. Horses find these uncomfortable and they have been known to slip round and cover one or both eyes (particularly when the horse is rolling). This can be extremely dangerous and for this reason I do not recommend them.

The foot and shoeing

Often the feet of horses at grass are neglected. Even if they are not shod, feet still require regular trimming to keep them in good shape and to guard against cracks. Horses are shod to prevent hooves cracking and to protect against excessive wear (particularly when the horse is doing road work) **(13)**. In the summer months, when the ground is hard, shoes also help to reduce the concussive effect on the joints of the limbs. Corrective trimming is often done to help correct conformational defects, improving the horse's action. This requires a qualified and experienced farrier. In Britain it is illegal for anyone to shoe a horse unless he is listed in the Register of Farriers. Horses who are prone to cracks need more regular attention from the farrier to prevent the hooves becoming long, splitting and out of shape. If possible, horses which are kept out permanently should have a dry area where they can stand so that the hooves do not become soft and crumbly. Many horse owners use hoof oil in the summer to prevent the hooves drying out and becoming brittle. This prevents the natural absorption and evaporation of moisture through the hoof wall. There are now alternative hoof-moisturising products

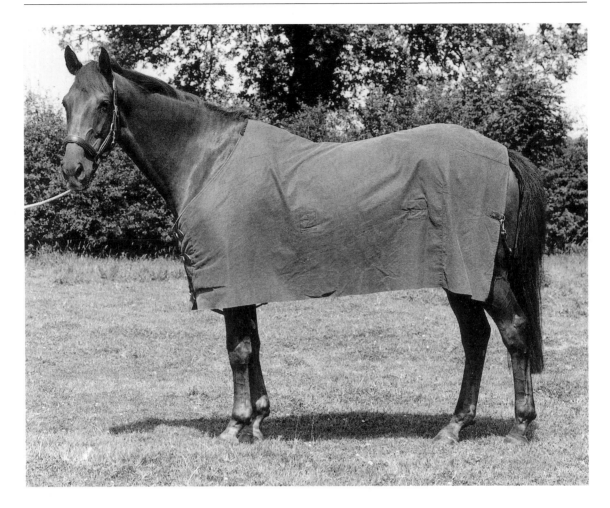

available which are more beneficial. Problems associated with the horse's feet are relatively common (see pp. 136–41). Puncture wounds of the foot are probably the most common cause of acute lameness.

11 A New Zealand rug must be correctly fitted so that it does not rub the horse and become uncomfortable

12 The leg straps must be attached properly so that the rug does not slip

13 (*Overleaf*) Horses may be shod in the summer months to prevent the feet from cracking when the ground is hard

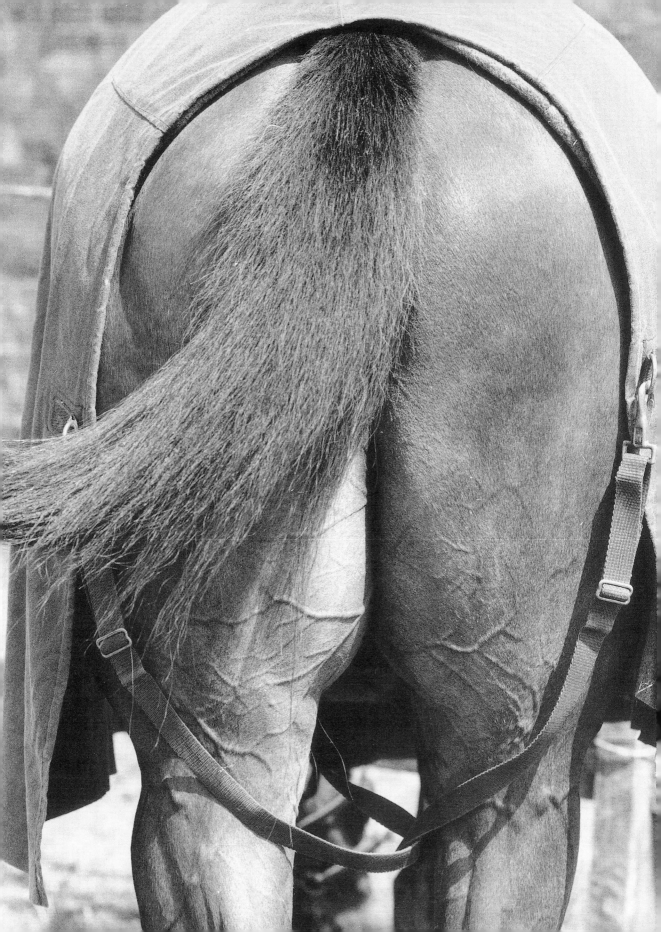

2
COPING WITH PARASITES

2
COPING WITH PARASITES

The importance of worming

All horses have worm infections and the aim is simply to keep the numbers as low as possible. It has been estimated that an adult horse may pass as many as 10 million worm eggs in their dung every day. These eggs on the pasture may then develop into larvae which at some stage in their development become infective to the horse. These infective larvae are taken into the horse as it grazes. The larvae (depending upon the species) then migrate through body tissues such as the blood vessels, liver, lungs and the gut lining (peritoneum) before returning to the horse's gut as adult worms where they lay eggs, so completing their life cycle. During the larvae migration, irreparable damage may be done to body tissues. Horses may develop colic, bronchitis, diarrhoea and cease to thrive. Sometimes, the blood vessels become weakened by the migration of larvae through them, and if this happens the damaged blood vessel may spontaneously rupture leading the horse to collapse, and even die. This most commonly happens when the horse is working hard and the blood vessels are under pressure. Young horses are particularly vulnerable as they have not been able to develop a natural tolerance against the worms.

Horses may become heavily parasitized by migrating worm larvae, even if wormed, particularly when sharing pastures with horses which have not been treated.

The severity of the worm infestation of a horse can be ascertained but it is not a simple exercise. Faecal egg counts (counting the eggs in a sample of dung) simply reflect the presence of egg-laying adult worms. The most accurate method of determining the extent of the parasite burden is by blood tests which can be carried out by the veterinary surgeon.

Some of the more common internal parasites of the horse are: large strongyles (redworm), small strongyles, ascarids (roundworms), bots, threadworms, pinworms, lungworms and tapeworms.

Horses are susceptible to different species of worms at different ages. For example, young foals are more likely to develop problems with ascarids and tapeworms, whereas adult horses are more seriously affected by redworms.

Large redworms
Large strongyles

The most important parasites of adult horses are the large redworm, otherwise known as the large strongyle. The large strongyles are colourless but appear red as they suck blood from the lining of the

Types of worms affecting horses of different ages	
Foal	threadworm
	large roundworm
3 years and under	large roundworm
	redworm
	small strongyles
	bots
	tapeworm
	lungworm
	pinworm
Adult	redworm
	small strongyles
	bots
	tapeworm
	lungworm
	pinworm

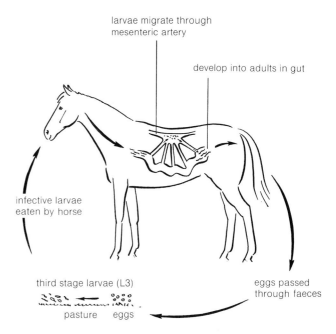

Fig. 9 Life cycle of *Strongylus vulgaris* (large redworm)

horse's gut. They are 2–8 cm (1–3 in) long.

Potentially, the most damaging of this group is *Strongylus vulgaris*. This species is particularly dangerous because of its migratory route through the mesenteric arterial system (the blood vessels which supply the gut). Here they may cause thrombosis, arteritis, and even aneurisms (bursting of the artery). It is thought that these worms may be responsible for 90 per cent of spasmodic colic cases. The life cycle of the large strongyles is shown in **Fig. 9**.

Eggs are laid by the adult worm in the large intestine and are then passed out in the droppings. These eggs can then remain viable (alive) for up to 12 months. The larvae develop from the eggs on the pasture in stages, and it is the third stage (L3) which is infective to the horse. Development of the larval stages depends on the climate but can be completed in about 10 days in warm, moist conditions. The L3 larvae crawl from the dung and collect on blades of grass where they have more chance of being eaten. They are repelled

by strong sunlight and so in these conditions they migrate down to soil level. Some moisture is needed for them to move, so very dry, hot conditions will kill the larvae. Shorter pasture will also render them more susceptible to the effects of the environment, and this can be beneficial in their control. The infective (L3) larvae are then eaten by the grazing horse and passed into the intestines. *Strongylus vulgaris* migrates extensively through the horse's body and eventually reaches the anterior mesenteric artery (with potentially disastrous results). Eventually the mature larvae return to the wall of the large intestine where they develop into egg-laying adults five to nine months after infection. Another of the large strongyles is *Strongy-*

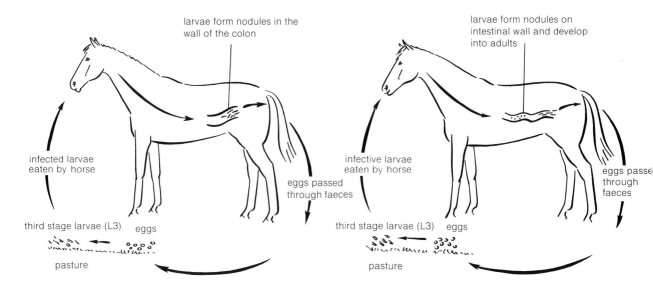

Fig. 10 Life cycle of *Strongylus edentatus* (redworm)

Fig. 11 Life cycle of small strongyles (small redworm)

lus edentatus. The life cycle of this worm is shown in **Fig. 10**. *Strongylus edentatus* live in the peritoneal lining of the abdominal cavity where they form nodules, which may be associated with bleeding.

The life cycle of the large strongyles makes them reasonably easy to control. There is evidence that an acquired immunity to *Strongylus vulgaris* infection develops in horses with age, but this does not mean that other control measures should not be taken.

Small redworms
Trichonema species

These include the *Trichonema* species and are the least pathogenic of the strongyle species. The eggs of the small strongyles are passed out in the dung where they develop into larvae. These are then ingested by grazing horses and develop in the wall of the large intestine. Damage to the horse may result here from the activity of the adult worms. They suck blood and may induce anaemia if the infestation is heavy (see **Fig. 11** for life cycle).

Roundworm
Ascarids

These large worms may be 30 cm (12 in) long and as thick as a pencil. The species is known as *Parascaris equorum* and it can have serious effects, particularly on foals, yearlings and horses under three years of age. Foals have very little, if any, immunity to roundworms, and infection can result in retarded growth, unthriftiness, weight loss and eventually death.

An adult female can lay up to 1 million eggs per day and these are very resistant to disinfectants and climatic conditions, enabling them to remain viable outside the horse for up to three years. The infective larvae develop inside the egg and when the egg is eaten by the foal the larvae hatch out into his gut. From here they burrow through the gut wall and migrate to the liver and lungs via the blood. The larvae are then coughed up from the lungs and swallowed back into the small intestine where they develop into egg-laying adults. The life cycle takes about eight to twelve weeks **(Fig. 12)**. With large infes-

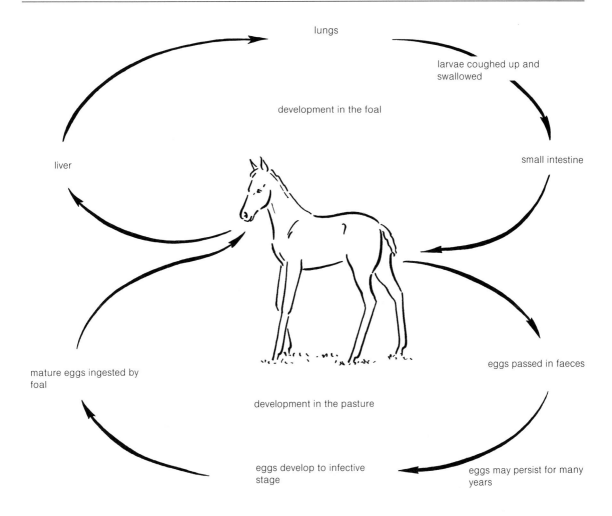

lungs

larvae coughed up and swallowed

development in the foal

liver

small intestine

mature eggs ingested by foal

eggs passed in faeces

development in the pasture

eggs develop to infective stage

eggs may persist for many years

Fig. 12 Life cycle of ascarids (roundworm)

tations, many of the adult worms die and are passed out in the dung. The adult worms can cause intestinal obstruction due to their size and may even cause a rupture of the gut.

Signs of roundworm infection include a high temperature, cough, nasal discharge, colic and unthriftiness.

Threadworms
Strongyloides westeri

Threadworms are common in foals under six months of age, although clinical symptoms of infection are rarely seen. This parasite can be passed from the mare via her milk, or it can penetrate the foal's skin and enter the body. The adult worms live in the small intestine and because they are very small are usually well tolerated by the foal. However, heavy infestations can cause scouring in foals two to four weeks old which may coincide with the mare's foaling heat. Foals can be treated for threadworm from seven days of age, but routine and thorough worming of the mare will help to reduce the incidence of infection. Threadworms are difficult to control with conventional wormers (except with high doses) and ivermectin is usually preferred. The life cycle of *Strongyloides westeri* is shown in **Fig. 13**.

Pinworm (seatworm)
Oxyuris equi

The *Oxyuris equi* is otherwise known as pinworm. Its infections are not usually serious but they may cause intense irritation of the anal region causing the horse to rub his tail excessively. These worms are white and round and are 1–10 cm ($\frac{1}{2}$–4 in) long. The adults live in the large intestine and the female lays her eggs on the skin around the anus causing the itching already mentioned. Larvae develop inside the egg and fall onto the pasture where they are ingested by grazing horses. The life cycle spans four to five months. They are easily killed by routine doses of wormer. Their life cycle is shown in **Fig. 14**.

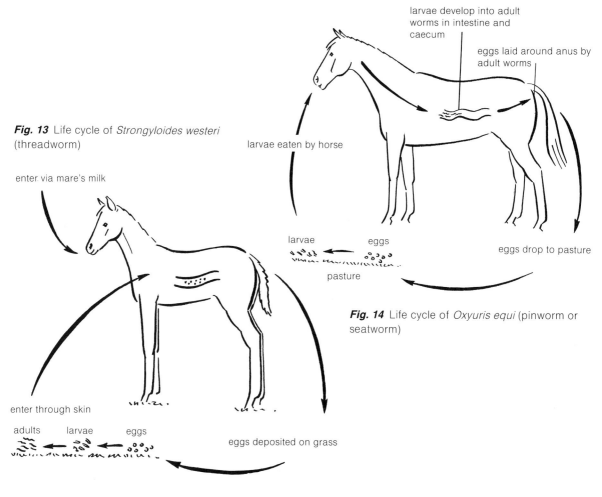

Fig. 13 Life cycle of *Strongyloides westeri* (threadworm)

Fig. 14 Life cycle of *Oxyuris equi* (pinworm or seatworm)

Neck threadworm
Microfilariae

These are of the *Onchocerca* species. Heavy infestations can be harmful to the horse causing restricted movement of the neck or forelegs. It is not a gut parasite but is found intertwined through connective tissue. Rather than laying eggs it gives birth to mobile embryos called *microfilariae*. These are extremely small and make their way to the neck and underside of the body where they congregate under the skin. They are killed by worming, but if large numbers are present there may be a reaction afterwards, manifesting itself as lumps on the neck and underbelly as the microfilariae die.

Tapeworm
Anoplocephala

The tapeworm, *Anoplocephala perfoliata*, is the only tapeworm found in horses in the UK. It is found on either side of the ileocaecal valve (the junction between the large and small intestines). This tapeworm has few clinical effects, but the site of attachment of the worm is often inflamed and ulcerated. The adult is segmented and about 8 cm (3 in) long and about 1 cm ($\frac{1}{2}$ in) wide. It sheds its segments, which contain eggs, and these are then passed out in the dung before being eaten by an intermediate host, namely forage mites. Larval development takes place within these mites which are then eaten by the horse whilst grazing, and the larval form develops directly into the adult in the caecum. This takes about 10 weeks **(Fig. 15)**. Few wormers are effective against tapeworm and so all horses should be treated with an effective wormer such as Strongid-P (pyrantel embonate), at double the normal dose.

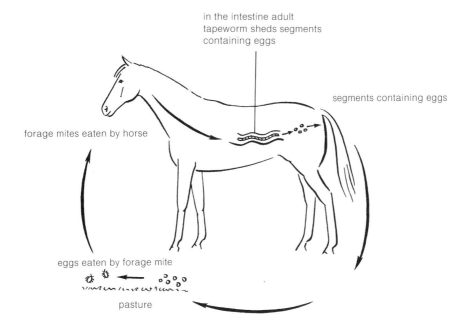

in the intestine adult tapeworm sheds segments containing eggs

segments containing eggs

forage mites eaten by horse

eggs eaten by forage mite

pasture

Fig. 15 Life cycle of *Anoplocephala* (tapeworm)

Lungworm
Dictyocaulus arnfieldi

Dictyocaulus arnfieldi is the only lung-worm which occurs in horses. It can cause acute coughing, but even badly affected horses may not always pass eggs or larvae out in their droppings, making diagnosis difficult. Infection is more common in donkeys who are able to carry large infestations of the worm without exhibiting any symptoms. It is not wise, therefore, to graze horses and donkeys together as the latter may act as symptomless carriers of lungworm creating a significant hazard to other horses. In the horse, migrating larvae rarely complete their development and often produce severe tissue reactions.

Fig. 16 Life cycle of the bot fly

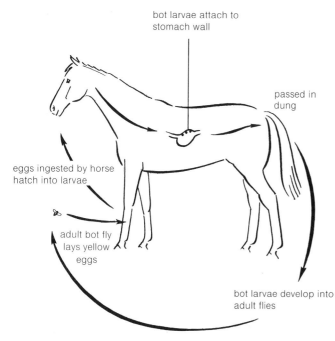

bot larvae attach to
stomach wall

passed in
dung

eggs ingested by horse
hatch into larvae

adult bot fly
lays yellow
eggs

bot larvae develop into
adult flies

Bots
Gasterophilus intestinalis

Bot flies are common around horses during the summer months. The adult bee-like flies do not sting or bite, but they lay the characteristic yellow eggs on the hairs of the horse's legs, shoulders and neck. They are then licked off and ingested by the horse. One of the most spectacular finds when post mortems are being conducted is the presence of bots in the pharynx, stomach, duodenum or rectum. These plump cylindrical creatures grow to some 2 cm (1 in) in length. They are often present in dozens, and sometimes even hundreds. The larvae usually hatch in the stomach and attach themselves to the stomach wall. They mature for 10–12 months, detach themselves and are then passed out in the dung where they pupate and turn into adult flies **(Fig. 16)**. Occasionally there may be so many bot larvae in the stomach that they cause colic, or even a rupture of the stomach wall, followed by death. Bot larvae are not normally killed by the common wormers, except ivermectin (Eqvalan) and a dose of this should be given at the end of summer (October/November) as a matter of course. Organophosphorus compounds can also be used but great care should be taken with them. They are used specifically to kill bot larvae in the horse's gut, and should not be administered to any sick horse or those suffering from liver disease.

Prevention and treatment of intestinal parasites

Worm control is one of the most important aspects of horse management. Horses may look healthy but still be carrying a heavy worm burden. Sadly, because worms cannot be seen, it is an area of horse management that is often neglected. Failure to implement an effective worm control programme will undermine all the other steps taken to ensure the horse's health. Well-fenced pastures, scientifically formulated diets, warm stables and shelters, care of the new born foal and pregnant mare may all be a waste of time if the worm-control programme is inadequate. The aim of control is to reduce the number of worms the horse is carrying. This is done by two methods;

1. The administration of drugs (anthelmintics).
2. Pasture management.

The administration of drugs

This is otherwise known as worming. There is a wide range of drugs available to kill worms (see table).

The ways in which the different drugs work are quite distinct from one another. However, the benzimidazole group all act in the same way on the adult worm which feeds on the blood and tissues of the horse's gut. The drug is taken into the horse's bloodstream and the feeding worm ingests it. It then acts upon the worm's body cells causing breakdown of the worm's gut and eventually death.

Eqvalan is also absorbed into the horse's bloodstream, and acts upon the

Drugs available for the control of internal parasites		
Trade Name	**Manufacturer**	**Active Ingredient**
Benzimidazole group		
Panacur	Hoechst	Fenbendazole
Telmin	Janssen Pharmaceutical	Mebendazole
Equizole	Merck Sharp & Dohme	Thiabendazole
Equitac	Smith Kline	Oxibendazole
Systamex	Wellcome	Oxfendazole
Other compounds		
Pony & Foal Wormer	Crown Chemicals	Piperazine
Strongid-P	Pfizer	Pyrantel embonate
Eqvalan	Merck Sharp & Dohme	Ivermectin
Organophosphorous compounds for worms		
Equivurm	Crown Chemicals	Haloxon
Organophosphorous compounds for bots		
Neguvon	Bayer	Trichlorfon
Equiguard	Shell Chemicals	Dichlorvos
Note Availability of trade name wormers will vary from country to country.		

worm's nervous system causing its paralysis. The dead adult worms are then passed out in the dung. Eqvalan is the only drug which also acts upon the migrating redworm larvae when given at the normal dose. This is a definite advantage with this drug.

Strongid-P (pyrantel embonate) is not taken into the bloodstream but stays in the gut and passes through the body wall of the worm causing paralysis. The worms are then evacuated in the dung.

Many horseowners like to rotate the use of wormers to reduce the chance of resistance of the worm to the drugs. As can be seen from the table *all* the benzimidazole group act in the same way, so interchanging wormers from this group will not prevent resistance.

Resistance There is no doubt that worms can and do develop resistance to anthelmintic drugs. Some of the worms have genetic characteristics which predispose them to develop resistance against certain classes of drugs, mainly the benzimidazoles. When a horse is wormed the majority of the adult worms are killed leaving a few survivors which continue to lay eggs. The most likely survivors are those who have the resistance genes. Inevitably, then, regular worming with the same drug will bring about a resistant population. Once resistance has developed it is irreversible and the drug becomes totally ineffective.

Nothing to date is known to be resistant to Eqvalan (ivermectin). Theoretically, it can therefore be used all the time. It is not wise to give ivermectin to a horse which has, or may have, a high worm burden (e.g. a horse who has recently arrived on a yard and whose previous worming history is unknown) because if there is a high incidence of migrating larvae, particularly in the blood vessels, they may cause harm. It is best, therefore, to use another wormer

such as Panacur to kill the adult worms first, and then move on to Eqvalan 10 days later.

As there are relatively few drugs which control worms, they should be used wisely. Proper use of these drugs and effective management will reduce the risk of resistance. One of the most important aspects of worm control is that *all* horses sharing the same pasture *must* be wormed at the same time. Worming the individual horses with different drugs at different times is a recipe for disaster and a total waste of money. If the horses belong to different owners an adequate worming programme should be devised, and strictly adhered to.

Other ways to reduce resistance and increase efficacy of the worming programme include:

- Worming new arrivals before they are turned out onto the pasture if at all possible.
- Giving the correct dose of wormer (i.e. following the instructions carefully).
- Removal of the dung from the pasture on a regular basis (see pasture management).

Designing a worming programme
Whilst designing an effective drugs programme for the horse there are a couple of factors which need to be considered:

- Only a double dose of Strongid-P (pyrantel embonate) will kill tapeworms.
- Only Eqvalan (ivermectin) will also kill bots.

It is therefore wise to include both these drugs in the worming programme. A double dose of Strongid-P should be given in early June and again in early October. A dose of Eqvalan should be given in November to kill the bot larvae in the stomach. Any of the wormers can be given for the rest of the doses but it does make sense to rotate the use of the different drugs. This can be done annually, e.g.

using Panacur and Strongid-P in alternating years. However, as discussed earlier, do not rotate with the benzimidazole group of drugs. A sample worming programme is given below:

March	normal dose
April	normal dose
May	
June	double dose of Strongid-P
July	normal dose
August	
September	normal dose
October	double dose of Strongid-P
November	Eqvalan

In the USA, many horse owners are now giving wormers daily in the feed. It has been suggested that this is a more efficient method of administering drugs in the fight against worms.

Pasture management to reduce the worm population

Horses may pass large numbers of worm eggs onto the pasture. There are various methods of reducing the worm numbers. These include resting the pasture, deep ploughing and reseeding, mixed grazing with other livestock and the collection of dung.

Rest Resting the pasture is an effective way of cleaning it. Resting from the previous autumn through the winter until the spring will help to significantly reduce the larval population. After the pasture has been grazed in the spring it may then be used for hay or silage before it is used again for grazing.

Ploughing This relies on the fact that parasite eggs and larvae will be deeply buried and therefore unable to survive. In fact, this is unlikely to be very effective, and resting the pasture is still preferred.

Rotational grazing This involves the use of at least three paddocks. One is grazed by sheep or cattle, the other by horses, and the third for hay, silage or rest. The following year they are all moved round **(Fig. 17)**. Rotation uses the principle of mixed grazing most effectively. It is

Fig. 17 Rotational grazing involves the use of at least three different paddocks, rotated between horses, cattle and conservation

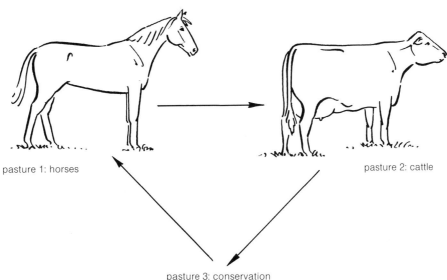

pasture 1: horses

pasture 2: cattle

pasture 3: conservation

known that cattle and sheep are not hosts to the same parasites as horses, and vice versa. Worm larvae which live in horses will be ingested by the cattle and sheep and killed off in the digestive tract. One exception to this is *Trichostrongylus axei* which is able to live in both horses and cattle. Fortunately, this worm does not seem to be particularly damaging to horses although heavy infestations are harmful to cattle.

Dung collection The most effective method of reducing the worm population

14 The most effective method of reducing the worm population of pasture is to remove the droppings on a daily basis

of pasture is to remove droppings on a daily basis **(14)**. Recent studies in the UK at the Animal Health Trust in Newmarket showed that horses divide their grazing areas into 'roughs' and 'lawns'. The roughs are where horses tend to dung and the lawns where they graze, unless the quality of grazing is very poor and the roughs have to be grazed too. As a result the lawns are always shorter. Research showed that the roughs contained 15 times more worm larvae than the lawns. This behavioural pattern is of considerable help in reducing the worm population. This is significant because there are several different schools of thought on harrowing the pasture. Harrowing spreads the larvae over the lawns as well as the roughs and the horses will therefore ingest more of them. When the weather is very hot and dry, harrowing will help to kill off the larvae although it may not be very effective in killing the worm eggs. These eggs will not hatch into larvae until the conditions are right, i.e. warm and damp, but when they do occur the eggs will hatch into larvae on the lawn areas and the horse will have no choice but to graze on them. Harrowing should only be done under the right conditions and then the pasture must be rested afterwards or grazed by other farm livestock first.

In some trials, removal of dung has been shown to be more effective than treatment with anthelmintic drugs. For large areas vacuum-hoovering machines can be used to remove the dung – far easier than manual collection with a wheelbarrow and spade! Horse manure should never be spread on to pasture used by horses for grazing, as eggs and larvae will be dispersed over the grazing areas.

The number of worm larvae on the pasture follows a seasonal cycle. If the summer months are warm and wet the larvae can migrate more easily to the edges of the grazed lawn areas. Research has shown that in May and August/September the faecal egg count rose substantially. Two to four weeks later the number of infective larvae from these eggs rose. It follows therefore that grazing horses are most at risk at the end of June, September and October. Worming in spring, early summer and early autumn has a greater effect on reducing the number of larvae. Researchers have also found that no amount of drug treatment will reduce high levels of infective larvae once they have reached substantial numbers. If this happens the pasture must be rested for six to 12 months.

As foals and yearlings are the most susceptible to worm damage their paddocks must receive particular attention. Mares are the source of infection for these foals and although they have to share the pasture with their dams, barren, pregnant and maiden mares should not be grazed on pasture for foals and yearlings. This is an important aspect of stud management.

Flies

There are a huge variety of troublesome flies throughout the world, and they can irritate horses in several ways: loss of condition, introduction of infections to small wounds and the eyes, as well as spreading infections from horse to horse. They also have a high nuisance factor!

House flies
Musca domestica

House flies are attracted to the moist parts of the body such as the nose, vulva, prepuce and wounds. They are particularly attracted to tears from the eyes where they may cause ulcerative dermatitis. Although these flies do not bite, they can cause severe aggravation as they tend to be present in large numbers.

Stable flies
Stomoxys calcitrans

Stable flies are a considerable nuisance because, as well as sucking the horse's blood, their saliva may cause an allergic reaction. It is the female in all species of biting fly which bite as they need a high-protein meal (blood) before laying their eggs, while the male feeds on plant juices. Unfortunately they are widespread and abundant, breeding in organic material such as bedding and muck heaps. The bite is painful and often leaves raised lumps on the horse's skin. These flies also bite humans and dogs.

Horse flies
Tabanus

Horse flies have a particularly painful, deep bite. It has blade-like slashing mouthparts which create a pool of blood on which it feeds. They cause much anxiety amongst horses who will gallop around in order to get away. Horse flies also transmit the disease equine infectious anaemia.

Bot flies

Bot flies irritate horses as they lay their characteristic yellow eggs on the horse's skin, and again you will often see horses galloping-around to get away.

Control of fly irritation

There are various methods for reducing numbers of flies and the irritation that they cause, although obviously they cannot be eradicated altogether.

Many flies breed on muckheaps which, if they are built properly, will kill many of the flies developing there by the sheer heat generated inside. The surface could also be regularly sprayed with insecticide. There are fly repellants which contain chemicals known as pyrethroids. These can be very useful on a daily basis if the instructions are followed carefully. Many horses strongly object to the application of fly sprays to any part of the body. In these cases the liquid should be sprayed onto a sponge or cloth before it is applied to the horse.

Insecticidal wound powders and creams are also available and will stop wounds becoming fly bound. More recently, browbands containing insecticide have come on the market and these are attached to the headcollar or bridle, spreading insecticide over the horse's body. They remain active for several weeks. Cattle tags containing insecticide may also be used in this way.

Fly fringes for protecting the horse's eyes may also be purchased, but beware of some fly masks as flies occasionally get under the mask and cause acute distress (15). A summer sheet will also protect much of the horse's body, particularly from biting flies (16).

A good field shelter provides excellent relief as flies do not tend to follow horses inside. If a shelter is not available and the horses are distressed they can be stabled during the day and turned out at night. This management procedure is adopted by many yards in the summer months.

15 A fly fringe will help protect the horse's eyes in the summer months

16 A summer sheet can offer some protection from biting flies

Examples of insecticides used for horses			
Organophosphate derivatives			
Fenithrothion	Durakill	dust	treatment of fly breeding areas and buildings
	Coopers Residual spray	liquid	
Lodofenphos	Nuvanol	spray	treatment of fly breeding areas and buildings
Pyrethroids			
Pyrethrin	Flyban	spray	fly repellant on horses
	Coopers Veterinary insecticide	spray	
Permethrin	Stomoxin	spray	fly repellant on horses, treatment of buildings
	Coopex	spray	
Cypermethrin	Rycopel	spray	fly repellant on horses
	Cyperkill	spray	

Note Availability of trade name drugs will vary from country to country

Part 2
NUTRITION AND FEEDING

3

DIGESTION AND NUTRIENTS

Grazing

There is much misunderstanding regarding equine feeding behaviour. Many domestic horses are not allowed to feed naturally, being stabled for most of the time. Wild horses spend up to 60 per cent of their day feeding **(Fig. 18)**, grazing up to midnight and then starting again at dawn. The passage of food into and through the digestive tract is slow, to suit this natural pattern of eating little and often. This is known as trickle feeding **(17)**. Horses eat much more slowly than cattle and their digestive system is very different. The natural feeding pattern of the horse involves endless and varied grazing. There seems to be a maximum and minimum time that the horse will spend grazing, and although there are other factors involved, such as grass quality, this time seems to be an integral part of the horse's behaviour. It therefore follows that even when horses are grazed on top-quality pasture they will not stop eating when they have had enough! Similarly, horses on bare paddocks will not eat for twenty-four hours a day but will stop after a certain time and eventually lose weight. When we stable the horse (even if it is only overnight), we restrict this integral pattern, often creating problems as a result.

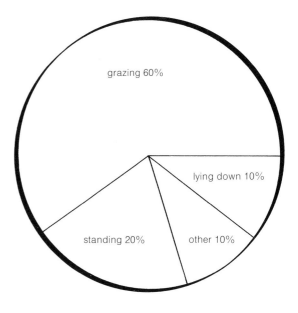

Fig. 18 Grazing behaviour of horses

The horse is unique and differs from other herbivores in that he has a small, single stomach (ruminants such as cattle and sheep have four stomachs), and a fermentation area at the posterior, or back end, of the gut **(Fig. 19)**. Ruminants have their fermentation area at the anterior, or front end, before the small intestine. This is significant because the small intestine is the major site of absorption of nutrients. Thus, ruminants are much more efficient at removing and absorbing nutrients from their food than horses.

17 The natural feeding pattern of the horse involves many hours grazing, taking in small amounts of food over a long period. This is known as trickle feeding

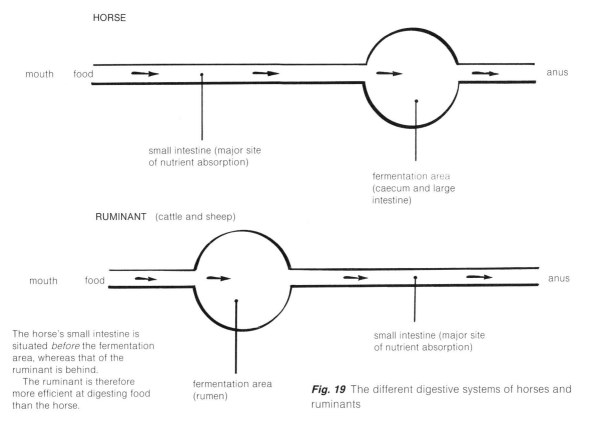

The horse's small intestine is situated *before* the fermentation area, whereas that of the ruminant is behind.

The ruminant is therefore more efficient at digesting food than the horse.

Fig. 19 The different digestive systems of horses and ruminants

The gut itself is simply a muscular tube with glands which secrete digestive juices to help break down the food into its constituent nutrients. These are then absorbed into the blood system. The tube is approximately 30 m (100 ft) long and is looped and coiled to fit into the abdominal space. There are several changes in diameter and direction of the gut, and these can be prone to blockages, e.g. the pelvic flexure **(Fig. 20)**.

The horse's digestive system consists of the mouth, oesophagus, stomach, small intestine, caecum, colon and rectum **(Fig. 21a,b)**.

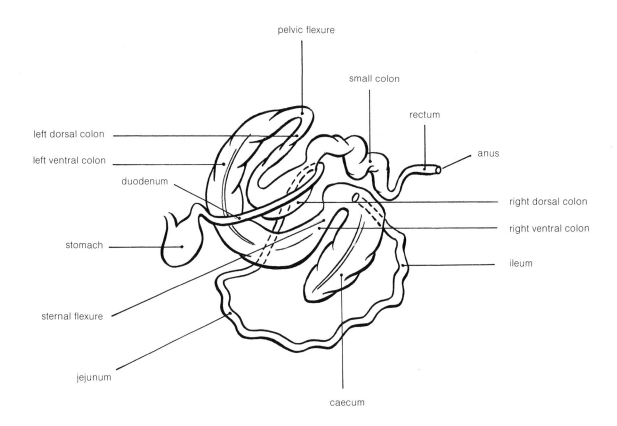

Fig. 20 Digestive system of the horse, showing the position of the main flexures

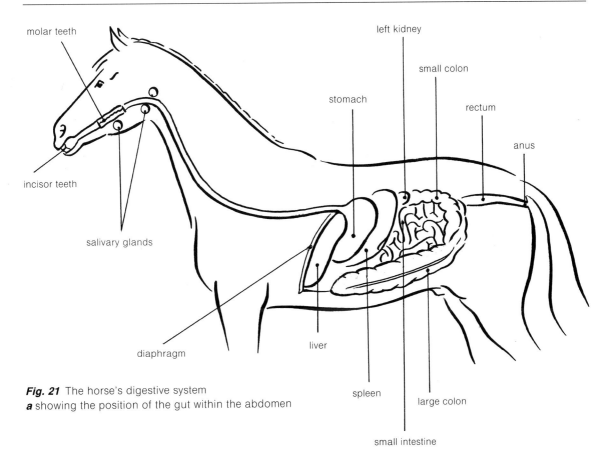

molar teeth

incisor teeth

salivary glands

diaphragm

stomach

left kidney

small colon

rectum

anus

liver

spleen

large colon

small intestine

Fig. 21 The horse's digestive system
a showing the position of the gut within the abdomen

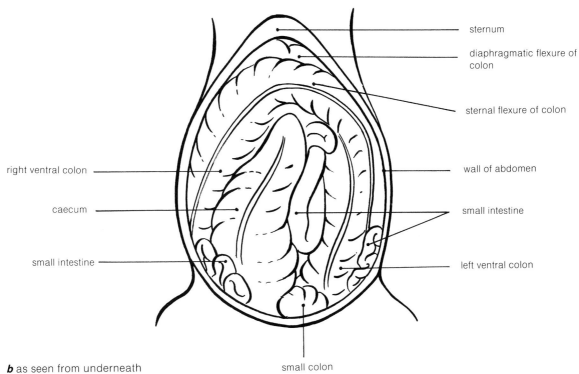

sternum

diaphragmatic flexure of colon

sternal flexure of colon

right ventral colon

wall of abdomen

caecum

small intestine

small intestine

left ventral colon

b as seen from underneath

small colon

Mouth

The horse grazes by selecting food with his lips then cropping it with his incisors. If the jaws are over- or under-shot (i.e. the upper and lower incisors do not meet properly) then grazing can be difficult, particularly on short pastures. The food is passed via the tongue to the back of the mouth for chewing by the molar teeth **(Fig. 22)**. Equine teeth differ from human ones in that they grow continually throughout the life of the horse. This is due to the constant grinding action, and therefore wearing down, of the molars. The molars have ridged surfaces to help grind the food. The upper jaw is wider than the lower one in order to provide overlap at the sides. This can cause sharp edges to appear which is why the teeth should be checked regularly by the equine dentist or veterinary surgeon and the sharp edges rasped down **(Fig. 23)**. Fibrous food, such as hay, needs more chewing than concentrates, and all food needs to be ground down to a minimum 2 mm in length before swallowing.

Horses produce about 10–12 litres (3 gal) of saliva per day. This lubricates the food as it passes into the oesophagus (a long thin muscular tube which attaches the mouth to the stomach). Sometimes food becomes lodged in the oesophagus and 'choke' can occur. If the situation does not correct itself within ten minutes call the veterinary surgeon. The bolus of food is then passed along the digestive tract by waves of muscular contractions known as peristalsis.

Fig. 22 Sections of the skull showing the positions of the teeth and roots

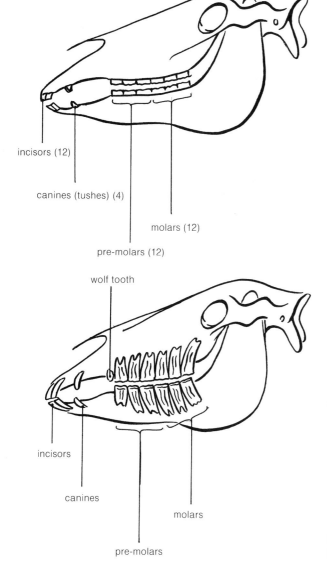

incisors (12)

canines (tushes) (4)

molars (12)

pre-molars (12)

wolf tooth

incisors

canines

molars

pre-molars

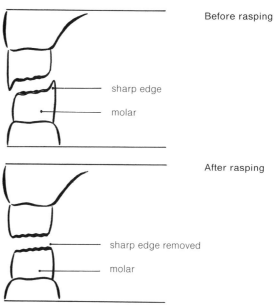

Before rasping

sharp edge

molar

After rasping

sharp edge removed

molar

Fig. 23 The effect of rasping (floating) the horse's teeth

Stomach

The stomach consists of a muscular sac **(Fig. 24)**. Its capacity in relation to the overall size of the horse is very small indeed. It holds about 7–9 litres (2 gal), and the empty stomach is about the size of a rugby ball. If you feed more than half a standard bucket of concentrates, food will be passed out of the stomach faster than normal, before it has been fully acted upon by digestive juices. This is a potentially dangerous situation. A full stomach will also press onto the diaphragm (the muscular sheet which separates the gut from the lungs), and if the stomach is full the lungs will not be able to expand to their full capacity. This is why horses should not be worked shortly after a feed. Also, working a horse at this time will result in blood being diverted away from the gut to the muscles, and this in turn will lead to inefficient digestion.

Because of the J-shape of the stomach, water tends to wash over the food rather than wash it out **(Fig. 25)**. This is a common misconception amongst horse owners and there is simply no need to restrict water whilst a horse is feeding.

The cardiac sphincter valve (see **Fig. 24**) is a very powerful one. Once food has passed into the stomach it cannot be regurgitated back; so unlike humans the horse cannot vomit. This means it has to be particularly careful in its selection of food.

The stomach is an acidic environment and this is where fermentation begins. However, it spends only a short time here and so little if any actual digestion takes place.

Small intestine

Food passes into the small intestine from the stomach through another valve called the pyloric sphincter. The small intestine consists of three distinct parts: the duodenum, jejunum and ileum. The length of this section of the gut is about 25 m (70 ft) and this is the primary site for food breakdown and absorption of nutrients (excluding the fibrous part of the diet). The digestive enzymes which are secreted by the glands in the wall of the intestine and

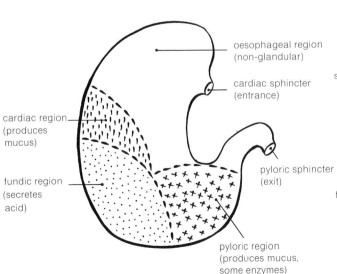

Fig. 24 The various different regions within the stomach

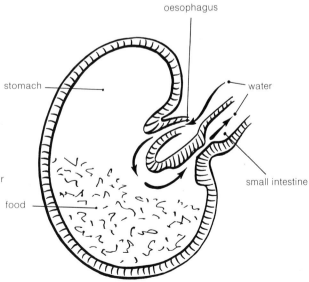

Fig. 25 The path taken by drinking water through the stomach, over the food contents

pancreas act upon protein, carbohydrate and fat. Digestion and absorption occurs along the length of the small intestine and food may pass along at the rate of one foot per minute. The digesta which passes from the small intestine to the large intestine consists of fibrous food residues and indigestible food.

Large intestine

This consists of the caecum, large colon, small colon and rectum. It is approximately 8 m (25 ft) long.

Caecum and large colon

Horses cannot digest the fibrous part of their natural herbage diet without the help of millions of microorganisms. These 'bugs' break down cellulose and other indigestible carbohydrates into energy-producing substances called volatile fatty acids. These are then absorbed and utilized by the horse. Cellulose is found in all plant cell walls, so without these bugs the horse could not digest grass properly.

The type and number of microorganisms in the gut depends upon the type of food being eaten by the horse. A horse being fed concentrates will have a different microbial population than one which is grazing only. These organisms are very sensitive to sudden changes in diet, so it is vital to keep the diet consistent. Serious metabolic problems can result from a sudden change, particularly in the concentrate part of the diet. Problems include, colic, diarrhoea, constipation and even laminitis.

Horses which have received antibiotic therapy will have a reduced bacterial population and this can cause problems. It can take a long time for the normal population to recover naturally. In these circumstances a course of probiotics may be given after the antibiotic therapy is completed. These are live microbial feed supplements and consist of known beneficial bacteria. They are protected so that they can bypass the acidic stomach environment and pass into the large intestine where they colonize. Young foals have to establish a bacterial population themselves and they often do this by eating their dam's dung. This is known as *coprophagy*. A course of probiotics at this time will ensure a healthy population of microorganisms. These bacteria produce many of the B vitamins, but how many of these are absorbed is not known.

Nearly all digestion of the fibrous part of the diet takes place in the caecum and large colon. The caecum has a capacity of about 30 litres (7 gal), and is a blind-ended sac. It is comma shaped and lies along the floor of the abdomen. A grazing horse will have a full caecum, giving an inflated appearance of the underbelly. This deflates when the horse is stabled overnight. The caecum is often described as a large fermentation vat and is where most of the bacterial breakdown occurs.

The large colon is about 3 m (12 ft) long and is folded to fit into the abdominal space. Its diameter reduces dramatically in places and these points are prone to blockages.

The digesta reaches the caecum about three hours after a meal and stays in the large intestine for about 45 hours.

The small colon

This is about 3 m (12 ft) long and is fairly narrow. It lies with the small intestine and is fairly free to move about. This may cause problems such as a twisted gut. Most of the water is re-absorbed from the digesta here, before the undigested food residues and dead bacterial cells are moved to the rectum where the characteristic balls of dung are formed, prior to evacuation through the anus.

Nutrients

The suitability of a diet for a horse should be determined not so much by the type of feeds it includes but rather what those feeds contribute in the way of nutrients.

Nutrients are substances which are vital for life and a diet which contains the correct balance of nutrients for the work level, or stage of reproduction, will result in improved health and performance.

Water

Approximately 70 per cent of the body-weight of an adult horse is made up of water. This increases to 75–80 per cent for a foal.

Water is required for many different life functions including:

- Temperature regulation.
- A medium in which chemical reactions can take place.
- A solvent in which substances can be dissolved and transported.
- Helping to give cells their shape.
- Excretion in the form of urine.
- Mare's milk.

Horses should have an ample supply of clean, fresh water at all times, especially during phases of growth, lactation and work. Water is the most vital nutrient for life. The amount consumed will to some extent be dependent on the amount of dry feed the horse is consuming. The horse at grass takes in much more water than a stabled horse, as grass contains about 75–80 per cent moisture. Horses should not be allowed to drink large quantities whilst they are hot from work. After hard exercise, let the horse cool down for 15–20 minutes before giving access to water, or alternatively allow only a couple of litres ($\frac{1}{2}$ gal) initially and then repeat 10 minutes later. Carry on until the horse is back to normality. Do not give a hot horse very cold water as this may cause colic.

As previously mentioned, water tends to flow over the stomach contents after drinking, rather than washing them out. It is therefore quite safe to allow the horse access to water whilst feeding. A mare which is in peak lactation (milk production) may produce as much as 12 kg (26 lb) water daily in her milk and this needs to be replaced.

Carbohydrate

This is simply a term used to include certain chemical compounds containing carbon, hydrogen and oxygen (carbo–hydrate). There are simple and complex carbohydrates. Animals take in some of the complex ones and break them down in the digestion process into simple sugars which are then absorbed. These are then built up in the body into other complex carbohydrates such as glycogen, which is then stored for later use. Carbohydrates are a major source of energy. Carbohydrate and fat both provide energy for the horse but in different ways. Protein is not a major energy source.

Carbohydrates include starch, sugars and cellulose (fibre). If the horse takes into the body more carbohydrate than it needs, it will store some as glycogen and convert the rest to fat (lipids).

Plants are able to make complex chemical substances from water, carbon dioxide and inorganic elements from the soil. The plant can trap solar energy from the sun and store it as chemical energy in the form of carbohydrates. This energy is then taken in by the horse and used for its own life processes. There are hundreds of different carbohydrates which occur naturally; however, they can be roughly divided into two main groups:

Simple carbohydrates (non-structural) These include starch (cereal grains), glycogen (muscle stores) and sugars (glucose, lactose etc.).

Complex carbohydrates (structural)

These include cellulose and lignin which are found in plant cell walls. Carbohydrate is stored as starch in plants, and as glycogen in the horse. Young plants contain large quantities of soluble carbohydrates and as they age over the summer months, the amount decreases. This is why grass over the winter months is much less digestible. It also contains more of the woody substance called lignin, which is indigestible to the horse.

Amazingly, horses themselves do not have the ability to digest cellulose, the major component of all plant (and there-fore grass) cell walls. Cellulose and hemi-cellulose are some of the constituents of fibre. To break down this complex carbohydrate, horses are totally reliant upon microorganisms in the hind gut. These bugs contain enzymes which can break down the cellulose into energy-giving substances called volatile fatty acids. These are then absorbed and used by the horse. Volatile fatty acids include acetic, propionic and butyric acid.

Grains such as oats, barley and maize are all high in starch, whereas grass, hay and other forages are fibre sources (for the various carbohydrate sources in the equine diet see **Fig. 26**). Carbohydrates are the main energy source for the horse.

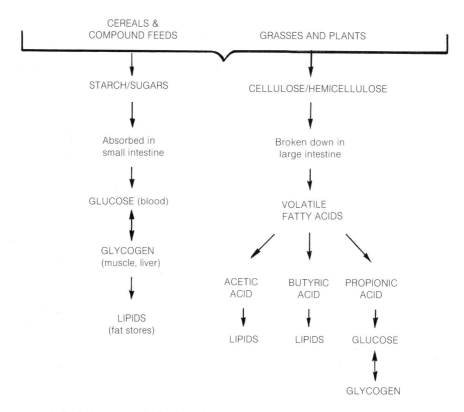

Fig. 26 Common carbohydrate sources in the horse's diet

Fat

Horses' diets are not naturally high in fat. In fact, they normally contain about 4 per cent.

Many horse owners, and trainers of performance horses, are increasing the fat content in the ration of horses in hard work. Fat contains 2.25 times more energy than carbohydrate. Recent research has shown that racehorses fed higher fat diets (in the form of added oil) had reduced fatigue and better recovery rates after races. Fat has also been used for a while to supplement diets of endurance horses with much success.

Fats can be converted to glucose (the main energy source of all living cells) through a highly complicated series of metabolic pathways in the horse's body. They can also be stored in fat cells called adipose tissue. This adipose tissue is the fat we humans spend ages trying to remove by dieting!

Fats contain fatty acids, some of which are essential in the horse's diet. Two such examples are linolenic and linoleic acids. If these are deficient then the horse may not grow or be able to reproduce.

The addition of 0.3 litres (1 cup) of oil to each of three feeds is equivalent to 1 kg (2.2 lb) of oats in terms of energy supplied. Oil should be of vegetable origin and polyunsaturated.

Protein

Protein is a most important component of all animal tissue. Without the synthesis of protein there could be no life.

The need for protein is greatest in the young growing horse. As he reaches maturity, only enough protein is required to replace worn body tissues and allow for the slow growth of tissue such as skin and hooves. It is highly unlikely that a mature horse will be deficient in protein, particularly if he has access to good grazing.

Proteins vary widely in composition, but their basic structure is made up of simple units or building blocks called amino acids. More than 20 of these amino acids occur naturally. The horse can make some amino acids himself and these are therefore known as 'non-essential', in that they are not required in his diet. Others he cannot make, and these are therefore required in the diet. These are known as 'essential' amino acids. The most important essential amino acids are lysine, methionine and tryptophan. Lysine is most likely to be deficient in the horse's diet, particularly when a cereal ration is being fed and the horse has limited access to good grass. All cereals are low in lysine.

Some proteins contain more of the essential amino acids than others and these are known as higher 'quality' proteins. Protein cannot be stored in the horse's body (unlike carbohydrates). Any excess has to be broken down and excreted in the urine or used as an energy source, albeit a highly wasteful and inefficient one. Except during starvation, protein is *not* a *main* energy source. This is a popular myth amongst horse owners. Horses in hard work need more carbohydrate and/or fat to provide the extra energy required. Only a small increase in protein is needed by hard-working horses; this is supplied simply by the increased quantities that the horse eats.

Vitamins

Vitamins are a group of chemical compounds which are vital for life. They are required in tiny quantities for the normal, healthy functioning of the horse's body. Nevertheless, a deficiency in the diet will produce problems. Some chemical compounds take on the function of vitamins after undergoing a chemical change and are known as provitamins, e.g. β-carotene changes into vitamin A. There are approximately 15 vitamins which are known to be essential to the horse but only the most important ones will be discussed. The vitamin requirements of the horse will depend upon individual circumstances, i.e. pregnancy, growth, level of work or age. Vitamins can be divided into two groups:

- Fat-soluble vitamins – vitamins A D E and K.
- Water-soluble vitamins – vitamin C and vitamin B complex.

Fat-soluble vitamins are so called because they can be stored in the fat deposits of the horse, and in the liver. Most of the fat-soluble vitamins are abundant in fresh herbage which means that the horse is able to take in enough in the summer months, and store them for use in the winter. Because they are fat soluble, feeding excess quantities, where horses are over-supplemented for example, will result in toxicity symptoms. The excess vitamins which are ingested are not broken down and excreted, as is the case with the water soluble vitamins.

Many of the water-soluble vitamins are made by the microorganisms in the gut (see page 52). However, how many of these are actually absorbed is not known. Presumably an appreciable quantity are taken into the horse's system as they are not stored. Excess water-soluble vitamins will be broken down and excreted in the urine. Overdosing with this group is not therefore as much of a problem. When horses are worked hard they need more of the water-soluble vitamins and so they should be supplemented. With sick or injured horses which are housed, and do not have adequate access to good grazing, supplementation will also be required, particularly with the B group of vitamins. In general, if good quality pasture or forage is available and the horse is not sick or in

hard work, then a vitamin supplement should not be necessary. It is important to note that hay loses its entire vitamin content within six months of storage.

Fat-soluble vitamins

Vitamin A (retinol) This vitamin is important for vision, bone development and energy metabolism. A deficiency of vitamin A can result in poor growth, weight loss, loss of appetite and reduced resistance to infections. As previously mentioned, vitamin A is produced from the provitamin β-carotene which is found in green grass. The amount of β-carotene in conserved forage such as hay can be determined roughly by the amount of green colour present.

In addition, the liver stores sufficient vitamin A to supply the horses needs for three to six months. Cereal grains contain little or no β-carotene except for maize (corn). Good sources of vitamin A include cod liver oil, and of course green herbage.

Vitamin D (calciferol) Vitamin D is intimately involved with the metabolism of the major minerals calcium and phosphorous, and is therefore required for bone development and maintenance. It is also needed for the formation of a substance called calcium binding protein, which aids in the absorption of calcium and phosphorous from the horse's gut into the body. Vitamin D is of vital importance in maintaining the blood levels of calcium. If it is deficient, calcium will not be absorbed from the gut and bone reabsorption of calcium will also be depressed. This will result in a fall of blood calcium. This will cause rickets in young horses and osteomalacia in adults. These conditions involve a loss of appetite and shifting lameness from one leg to another. The joints become swollen and there is an increased risk of bone fractures.

Vitamin D is made in the horse's skin in the presence of sunlight from two provitamins commonly found in forage. Rugged or stabled horses may therefore need supplementation. If at all possible the horse owner should allow the horse to graze with the sun on his back without the interference of rugs.

The mare's first milk, colostrum, is a rich source.

In the USA, there are several plant species which affect the metabolism of vitamin D, one of which is *Cestrum diurnum*, a member of the potato family. This plant grows in sub-tropical states including Florida, Texas and California. In grazing areas where this plant is rife horses will develop rickets and osteomalacia. No such plants occur in the UK.

Vitamin E (α-tocopherol) Vitamin E is derived from tocopherol. The horse's ability to store vitamin E is not as good as for vitamin A. Signs of a deficiency include a wide variety of problems such as infertility, pale areas of skeletal and heart muscle, and anaemia. Symptoms of deficiency will accelerate if the diet is also low in the trace element selenium, because both vitamin E and selenium work together (synergistically) in 'mopping up' toxic substances produced by working muscles. If the diet is high in unsaturated fats, perhaps where the horse is on a high-fat ration, then the amount of vitamin E must be increased. Horses in hard work have a higher vitamin E requirement. Alfalfa, green fodder and cereal grains are all rich sources of this vitamin.

Vitamin K This vitamin is essential for normal blood clotting. It is made by the bacteria in the horse's gut and a deficiency is therefore rare. It is common in leafy materials, for example alfalfa, and no supplementation is needed. It was once thought that vitamin K deficiency was responsible for 'bleeders', i.e. horses which suffer from airway bleeding during or after hard exercise. However, vitamin K therapy has not produced any beneficial effects in these cases.

Water-soluble vitamins

Synthesis of the water-soluble vitamins in the gut by the microorganisms seems to meet the horse's normal requirement. Horses which may benefit from supplementation of these vitamins are those in hard work, sick and injured horses, or older animals after antibiotic therapy. Water-soluble vitamins include:

- vitamin B_1 (thiamin)
- vitamin B_2 (riboflavin)
- vitamin B_6 (pyridoxine)
- vitamin B_{12} (cyanocobalamin)
- folic acid
- pantothenic acid
- choline
- biotin
- vitamin C (ascorbic acid)
- inositol
- niacin

The most commonly used of these vitamins are biotin, vitamin B_{12} and vitamin C.

Biotin Biotin has been used to improve the quality of crumbly, flaky hooves with varying success. Supplementing the diet with this vitamin will only be successful if the condition has been caused by the fact that the horse's gut microorganisms are not healthy enough to make biotin, e.g. if the horse is receiving (or has recently received) antibiotic therapy, or has acute or chronic diarrhoea.

It may well be that the diet is lacking the other nutrients which are also helpful in maintaining hoof growth and structure. These include zinc, calcium and the amino acid, methionine. A supplement should therefore include all these nutrients.

Vitamin B₁₂ (cyanocobalamin) This vitamin contains cobalt and thus a deficiency of cobalt will result in a deficiency of vitamin B_{12}. There is no evidence that supplementation with this vitamin improves performance of hard-working horses, although it is often used for this purpose.

Vitamin C (ascorbic acid) Vitamin C is required for formation of tissue (collagen). Fortunately, like most species of farm animals, horses can make their own vitamin C from glucose when it is required. It is made in the tissues themselves. Low blood levels of vitamin C have been found in horses with post-operative infections, epistaxis (nosebleeds), strangles and rhinopneumonia.

Horses are not very efficient at absorbing vitamin C from the gut when it is fed as a supplement. The only adequate method of supplementation has been shown to be by intravenous injection.

To summarize, if the horse is healthy, not under any stress and has access to good quality forage/pasture then vitamin supplementation should not be necessary. Horses under special stresses, or those who have received antibiotic therapy, will benefit.

Minerals

Minerals are inorganic substances found throughout the horse's body and are essential for health and development. Exact mineral requirements of the horse are still being determined, but at present at least 21 minerals are known to be required in the diet. Some minerals are required in relatively large amounts and are known as macrominerals. These include calcium, phosphorous, magnesium, potassium, sulphur, sodium and chloride (salt). Others are needed in minute quantities and are known as trace minerals or trace elements. These include iodine, cobalt, copper, iron, zinc, selenium, manganese, fluorine and chromium. Usually, trace minerals are present in a concentration of 50 milligrams per kilogram (mg/kg) or less. Nickel, vanadium and tin are minerals recently described as being necessary for the horse.

The horse's mineral intake will be greatly dependent upon the water and soil mineral content of the area. Other important factors are the hay to grain proportion and feed quality. Pasture which is poorly fertilized, or maintained inadequately, may have toxic levels of some minerals and be deficient in others. The quantity of minerals required by the horse depends upon several factors including workload, age (young and old horses have higher requirements) and reproductive status, i.e. pregnancy and/or lactation.

Some minerals will interfere with the absorption of others from the digestive system, so that overfeeding of one may lead to a deficiency in another. An example of this is calcium and phosphorous. If phosphorous levels are high and calcium levels are normal/low then the horse will not absorb enough calcium from the gut. This is because phosphorous and calcium are absorbed at the same site and an excess of the former technically swamps the absorption area so that less of the latter can be absorbed.

It is possible to overdose horses with minerals. Selenium, copper and molybdenum supplementation should be undertaken carefully.

Macrominerals

Calcium and phosphorous These are normally considered together because of their close inter-relationship. They are both required for proper mineralization of bone and are vital for a strong skeleton. Bone ash contains approximately 36 per cent calcium and 17 per cent phosphorous.

Calcium is also needed for lactation, blood coagulation, and for efficient nerve and muscle function. Calcium deficiency is very common, particularly in horses fed a high-cereal diet as all cereals are low in calcium. This is a particular problem where young stock are concerned because they have greater requirements and can, therefore, suffer in the short and long term from weaker skeletons and problems with developmental orthopaedic disease (DOD).

All animals, including horses, have their own system for regulating calcium. Blood levels have to be maintained wherever possible. If the level begins to fall, a hormone is released from the parathyroid gland which, in a series of complicated steps, brings about the release of calcium in the bone stores until the normal blood level is restored. Unless the horse has a severe deficiency, blood levels are likely to be normal as they are maintained at the expense of bone.

Phosphorous is also required for energy metabolism. As cereals are all low in calcium they are also high in phosphorous. The horse requires a diet which has a calcium to phosphorous ratio of between 1.5:1 and 2:1. The calcium should never be lower than the phosphorous level in the diet, and with cereals this is the case. Supplementation with calcium, e.g. ground limestone flour (calcium carbonate), is therefore essential. Bonemeal should not be used as a calcium supplement with a cereal diet because it also contains phosphorous and therefore exacerbates the imbalance. Useful sources of calcium include alfalfa, leafy green foods and sugar beet.

Magnesium Magnesium is primarily found in bone – bone contains 0.8 per cent magnesium. It is also needed for normal cell metabolism, and nerve and muscle function. A deficiency is rare. Good sources include clover, alfalfa and linseed.

Potassium This is important in acid-base balance and fluid regulation. It is also required for carbohydrate metabolism. Forages are excellent sources of potassium, so a deficiency of this mineral is rare. Hard-working horses may lose a large amount of potassium in sweat and should therefore be given body salt (electrolyte) mixtures containing potassium.

Sodium and Chloride Like potassium, sodium is important for fluid regulation and acid-base balance. It is also required for the transmission of nerve impulses along the horse's nerves. It aids in the absorption of sugars and amino acids from the gut. A deficiency will result in dehydration and poor performance. As most cereals are low in sodium the diet should be supplemented with sodium chloride or common salt. A free-access salt lick is the best method, as adding salt to the feed of a horse whose sodium status is normal can make him go off his feed. Chloride is also closely associated with potassium and sodium, but it is unlikely to be deficient if the horse has access to salt.

Trace minerals

As previously mentioned these are required in minute quantities. They are normally measured in levels of parts per million (ppm). To give you a better idea, 1 pence is 1 ppm of £10,000.

Selenium Like vitamin E, selenium is an antioxidant which helps to remove potentially damaging toxic waste products from working tissues such as muscles. The requirement for selenium and vitamin E is increased if the horse is receiving a high-fat diet, e.g. the competition horse. A deficiency of this mineral has been associated with poor performance in race horses, as well as white muscle disease (muscular degeneration or muscular dystrophy), a condition occasionally seen in foals. There are areas in the UK where the soil is known to be selenium deficient, including Shropshire, some areas of the Welsh hills, Scottish borders, north Cornwall and even Newmarket, the centre of the British racing industry.

High levels of selenium result in toxicity, or poisoning, causing a loss of hair to the mane and tail, lethargy, stiff joints, and the horse may even lose its hooves. Toxicity is rare in Britain unless it results from over-zealous supplementation. It is not unknown for plants in other countries to accumulate selenium from the soil in toxic levels, e.g. milk vetch, woody aster and golden weed. These are known as seliniferous plants. They are most common in dry regions. If pasture is sparse horses will eat these plants. In this case they should be removed from the offending pasture.

Copper Copper is needed for bone formation, cartilage, elastin synthesis and hair pigment. This explains the characteristic loss of colour around the eyes making the hair grey and giving the horse 'spectacles'. Copper deficiency can also result in anaemia or even rupture of the major blood vessels. In growing young stock, copper deficiency has been implicated in Developmental Orthopaedic Disease (DOD). Studs should have their soil copper levels tested to check they are within the normal range. Copper interacts with zinc and molybdenum, so high levels of these minerals in the soil will result in an induced copper deficiency.

Zinc Widely distributed throughout the horse's body, zinc is found in high concentrations in epidermal tissues, such as skin and hair as well as bone, muscle, blood and internal organs. Again, zinc deficiency has been implicated in DOD, although this is more likely to be an induced deficiency from interaction with other trace minerals than an actual deficiency of zinc. A deficiency will result in lameness and bone abnormalities.

Iron Along with copper, iron has an essential role in the formation of the oxygen-carrying compound haemoglobin. Chronic blood loss, due perhaps to a heavy parasite burden, will result in anaemia. Mare's milk is low in iron, however an iron deficiency is unlikely as most feeds contain more than adequate levels.

Iodine Iodine is a component of the hormone thyroxine which is produced in the thyroid gland – approximately 75 per cent of the total iodine in the horse's body is found here. A deficiency will result in abnormal oestrus cycles and foals that are born weak. Goiter in foals has been reported due to an excessive intake of iodine from large quantities of seaweed fed to a pregnant mare, which may result in the death of the foal within his first 24 hours. Many studs use seaweed fertilizers on their pastures and these should not therefore be overused, or used with seaweed supplements.

Wood chewing Wood chewing or dirt eating is often associated with horses who are short of one or more minerals **(18)**. Some horses will chew each others' tails when fed a complete pelleted ration only. This could be as a result of too little 'long fibre' in the diet. Supplement the diet with adequate minerals and make sure that the horse receives an absolute minimum of 35 per cent long fibre (forage) in the diet.

18 Horses often chew wooden fences when they are
mineral- or fibre-deficient. This can then develop into
a habit

4
FEED RATIONS AND FORAGE

4

FEED RATIONS AND FORAGE

Formulating a ration

Formulating rations for horses is certainly a difficult job. However, horse owners should be able to check that the diet they are feeding their horse contains all the required nutrients in approximately the right amounts.

Unlike other farm animals, horses cannot have their rations scientifically calculated down to the last calorie as there are so many variables – there are hundreds of different breeds involved in such different types and amounts of work. Not only this, but some are stabled whilst others are kept outdoors, and the amount of pasture a horse eats will obviously determine how many concentrates should be fed. All

horses should be treated individually when assessing their ration.

Nutrient demand will also depend on: condition, work level, age, reproductive status, health, environment and management.

1. The bodyweight

This can be calculated by a weightape or weighbridge and a table of weights. The most accurate is the weighbridge but few horse owners have access to one of these, although they are now quite common at studs/breeding farms and racing yards.

How to work out a ration
There are eight basic steps to be taken and estimations to be made when working out a ration:
• The bodyweight of the horse
• The appetite of the horse
• The energy required for maintenance
• The energy required for work
• The forage to concentrate ratio
• Making the ration
• Checking the protein level
• Checking and adjusting the ration

Average bodyweights		
	Bodyweight	
Height (HH)	(kg)	(lb)
11	120–260	264–572
12	230–290	506–638
13	290–350	638–770
14	350–420	770–924
15	420–520	924–1144
16	500–600	1100–1320
17	600–925	1320–1595
These figures should only be used as a guideline.		

In this example of ration formulation a 500 kg (1,100 lb) horse will be used throughout.

2. The appetite

The adult horse will eat approximately 2.5 per cent of his bodyweight.

So to calculate the appetite, using a 500 kg horse:

$$appetite = 500 \times \frac{2.5}{100} = 12.5 \text{ kg (28 lb)}$$

Therefore, a 500 kg (1,100 lb) horse can eat 12.5 kg (28 lb) of food per day.

This equation is based on the dry matter of the food, excluding moisture content. As grass is high in moisture then horses will eat much more than 12.5 kg (28 lb) of grass per day.

3. The energy required for maintenance

Horses require energy just to support life systems such as breathing, moving and eating on a daily basis. This is before any work is asked of him. The bigger the horse the higher the maintenance requirement, thus the calculation is based on the bodyweight of the horse. Digestible energy is measured in MJ (mega joules).

energy for maintenance (MJ DE/day)

$$= 18 + \frac{\text{bodyweight (kg)}}{10}$$

$$= 18 + \frac{500 \text{ (kg)}}{10}$$

$$= 68 \text{ MJ DE/day}$$

So this 500 kg horse will require 68 MJ DE/day

4. The energy required for work

Obviously, this will depend upon the level of work. Individual work load is very difficult to assess, so a table of 'work scores' has been developed to assist you when calculating a ration.

Work scoring

Type of Work	Work Score	Extra energy required per day 500kg horse
1 hr walking	+1	10MJ DE/day
1 hr walking plus some trotting	+2	20MJ DE/day
1 hr including trotting and cantering	+3	30MJ DE/day
Schooling, dressage and jumping	+4	40MJ DE/day
Novice ODE or 1 day hunting per week	+5	50MJ DE/day
Intermediate ODE or 3 days hunting per 2 wks, Novice 3-day event	+6	60MJ DE/day
Advanced ODE, Intermediate 3-day event, hunting 2 days per week	+7	70MJ DE/day
Racing	+8	80MJ DE/day

In this example of a 500 kg horse who has a work score of +5, the extra energy required is calculated as follows:

$$\text{work score} \times \frac{\text{bodyweight}}{50}$$

$$= 5 \times \frac{500}{50}$$

$$= 50 \text{ MJ DE/day}$$

This is then added to the energy required for maintenance which we have already calculated in step 3 as 68 MJ DE/day

total energy required = 68 (maintenance) + 50 (work) = 118 MJ DE/day

5. The forage to concentrate ratio

Again, this depends upon the level of work the horse is doing. Horses who are in very hard work will require more energy from the concentrates than the forage and vice versa. This is estimated as a percentage of the total. (See table.)

Forage to concentrate ratios

Work score	Forage %	Concentrates %
Maintenance	100	0
1–2	75	25
3–5	60	40
6–7	40	60
8	30	70

So, for the 500 kg horse with a work score of 5, 60 per cent of his energy requirement will come from hay and 40 per cent will be provided in the concentrates.

energy from hay
$$\frac{118 \times 60}{100}$$
71MJ DE/day

energy from concentrates
$$\frac{118 \times 40}{100}$$
47MJ DE/day

Thus, the hay needs to provide 71MJ DE/day and the concentrates 47MJ DE/day

6. Making the ration

This step converts these figures into an actual ration. For this step we need to know the nutrients contained in some common feedstuffs. See table. The values in this table are only approximate and actual amounts can vary considerably.

Nutrient values of common feedstuffs

Feed	Crude protein %	MJ/kg
Concentrates		
Oats	10	11–12
Barley	9	13
Maize	8	14
Naked oats	13.5	16
Extracted soyabean meal	44	13.3
Peas	23	14
Wheatbran	15.5	11
Sugarbeet pulp	7	10.5
Vegetable oil	0	35
Compound feeds		
Horse and pony cubes (pellets)	10	9
Performance mix	13	12–13
Stud mix	15	11–12
Forage		
Hay average	4–8	7–8
Hay good	9–10	8–10
Hay poor	3–6	6–7

The 500 kg horse is to receive 71 MJ DE/day from hay. Assuming that the hay being used is of average nutritional quality and it contains 8MJ DE/kg, then the amount of hay to be fed per day can be calculated as follows:

$$\text{weight of hay} = \frac{71}{8}$$
$$= 9 \text{ kg (20 lb) hay per day}$$

The same step can be taken with the concentrates, in this case a performance mix is being fed which contains 13MJ DE/kg

weight of performance mix per day
$$= \frac{47}{13}$$
$$= 3.5 \text{ kg (8 lb) performance mix per day}$$

It is much simpler to use compound feeds. Not only have they been nutritionally balanced for you, but they eliminate the need to mix your own ration at home. Home mixing can be expensive and wasteful. So, 3.5 kg (8 lb) of concentrates and 9 kg (20 lb) of hay falls ideally within the horse's appetite of 12.5 kg (28 lb) per day. This is not always the case, particularly when low energy feeds are used. Some alteration and adjustments will then be required.

7. Checking the protein level

If you estimate the energy level in the ration carefully then the protein should look after itself, although this is not always the case. Pregnant stock, lactating and growing horses have a specific protein requirement which is vital for proper growth and development of the foal.

The 500 kg horse in medium work requires 8–9 per cent crude protein according to the above table. Does the ration of 3.5 kg performance mix and 9 kg of hay provide the horse with 8–9 per cent protein?

The protein requirements of horses	
Status	Crude Protein %
Light to medium work	8–9
Hard to fast work	9–11
Pregnant mare (1st 8 months)	8–9
Pregnant mare (last 3 months)	10–12
Lactating mare (1st 3 months)	12.5
Lactating mare (2nd 3 months)	10–12
Stallion	10
Foal 6 months	16
Yearling	13.5
Two year old	10

Hay 9 kg $\times$ 6% CP = 0.540 kg protein
Mix 3.5 kg $\times$ 13% CP = 0.455 kg protein
TOTAL = 0.995 kg protein
= 0.995 kg

The percentage protein in the ration is therefore: $\frac{0.995}{12.5} \times 100 = 7.96\%$

This is rounded up to 8% which meets the requirements.

8. Checking and adjusting the ration

Once a particular ration has been calculated and introduced slowly, then the horse should be monitored to check that he is not gaining or losing weight. If he is, alter the ration accordingly. In some cases the horse may need to gain or lose weight, but once the desired weight is achieved the ration must be re-adjusted. Some horses, known as 'good doers', will gain weight on a minimal amount of food and will need particular care and attention. If you know that your horse is in this category adjust the amount accordingly. The same follows for horses in poor condition who may require much more feed than the calculated amount to put on weight. Once this has been achieved reduce the concentrates back to a proper level.

Keep, feed or range blocks

These are products which are manufactured by feed companies for the purpose of providing the horse with nourishment. They are fed in conjunction with grazing and/or hay to provide a balanced ration. They are durable and weather resistant and are usually placed in a suitable container on the ground or hung from the fence. Horses are supposed to take as much as they need but in practice many horses over indulge. This can be expensive. Feed and keep blocks (known as range blocks in the USA) should not be confused with mineral blocks which *only* provide minerals and which are usually used all year round.

Grazing provides some horses with all their dietary requirements but for others, particularly those that are working, reproducing or growing, this may not be enough. The quality of grazing varies so much between pastures that it is impossible to estimate the amounts eaten, or nutrients consumed. This can be determined to some extent by the condition of the horse, and should be taken into account when determining how many, if any, extra concentrates and hay should be fed. Also, the variation in quality and quantity of the grass throughout the year (see page 71) should be taken into account.

Condition scoring

A horse's condition can be objectively assessed by using a method originally designed for agricultural livestock, namely Condition Scoring. This is worked out on a scale from nought to five, and involves a manual and visual estimation of the horse's weight displacement over the back, hind quarters, ribs and neck **(Fig. 27) (19)**. The amount of flesh covering these areas is the indicator and the estimations should then be evaluated by matching them to the table.

Fig. 27 Condition scoring of horses

condition score   back   pelvis

5

obese: large masses of fat carried on neck and quarters. Feel ribs on pressure. A marked neck crest, even in mares (5)

4

getting fat: bones difficult to feel (show horses) (4)

3

normal: hip bones and back vertebrae defined but not prominent (hunters/eventers) (3)

2

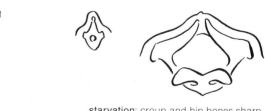

thin: bones prominent. Some muscle definition (2)

1

starvation: croup and hip bones sharp and prominent. Ribs prominent, lines down quarters either side of the tail (1)

19 This horse has a condition score of 5. He needs to lose some weight

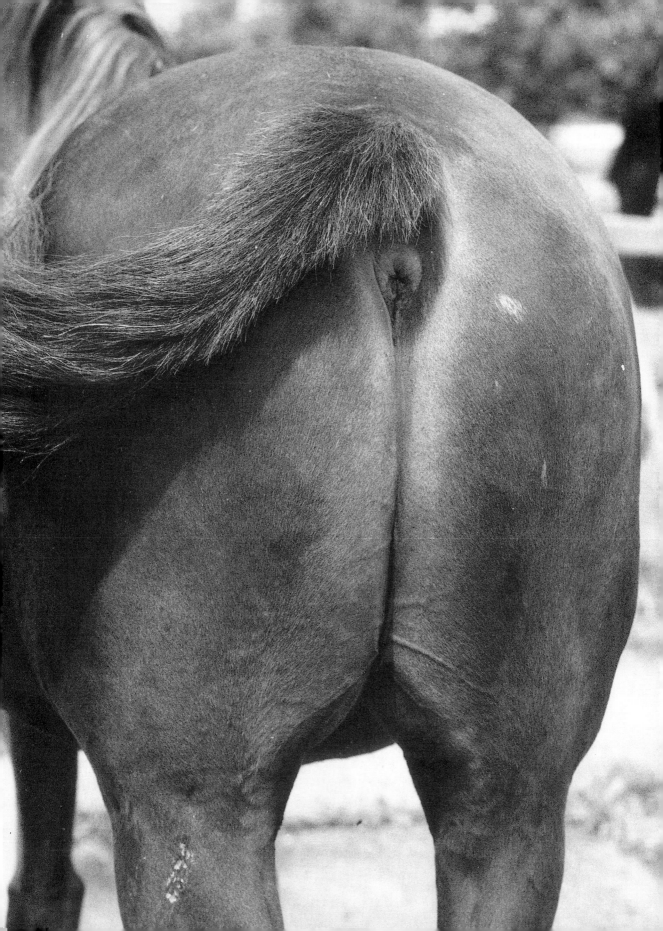

Condition scoring

Condition Score	Pelvis	Back and Ribs	Base of Neck
0	Deep cavity under tail and either side of croup. Pelvis angular. No detectable fatty tissue between skin and bone.	Processes of vertebrae sharp to touch. Skin drawn tightly over ribs.	Ewe neck, very narrow and slack at base.
1	Pelvis and croup well defined, no fat but skin supple. Poverty lines visible and deep depression under tail.	Ribs and backbone clearly defined but skin slack over the bones.	Ewe neck, narrow and slack at base.
2	Croup well defined but some fat under skin. Pelvis easily felt, slight depression under tail.	Backbone just covered by fat, individual processes not visible but easily felt on pressure. Ribs just visible.	Narrow but firm.
3	Whole pelvic region rounded, not angular and no gutter along croup. Skin smooth and supple, pelvis easily felt.	Backbone and ribs well covered but easily felt on pressure.	Narrow but with no crest (except stallions).
4	Pelvis buried in fat and only felt on firm pressure. Gutter over croup.	Backbone and ribs well covered and only felt on firm pressure. Gutter along backbone.	Wide and firm with folds of fat. Slight crest even on mares.
5	Pelvis buried in fat and cannot be felt. Clear deep gutter over croup to base of dock. Skin stretched.	Back looks flat with deep gutter along backbone. Ribs buried and cannot be felt.	Very wide and firm. Marked crest.

Conservation of forage for horses

Hay, silage and haylage are the three main types of conserved forage fed to horses in Britain. Haylage is becoming increasingly popular, particularly for those horses that compete regularly, and for those that suffer from COPD (p. 149). However, hay is traditionally the major forage source for stabled horses and those kept out in the winter months. Unfortunately, hay-making is dependent on the weather, and in Britain long, wet periods often delay the cutting of the crop. Some farmers now use barn-drying techniques where the hay is cut and brought into special barns where it can be dried quickly producing excellent results.

The aim when preserving forage is to cut the crop at the optimum time and prevent further life processes and enzyme action occurring, both in and on the crop. This will reduce losses and maintain the feed value of the crop after cutting. Hay is dried as quickly as possible to prevent fermentation, whereas haylage and silage production involve a fermentation process (pickling).

Grass growth throughout the year varies. During the summer the amount of water in the plants decreases (the dry matter increases). More importantly, the nutritional quality of the grass decreases as summer passes **(Fig. 28)**. Silage is cut at the beginning of the season when the moisture level is high; haylage is cut later than silage when the moisture level is lower; and hay is the latest cut. Hay is then further wilted and stored at a moisture level of 10–15 per cent (dry-matter 85–90%).

As a rough guide, silage is cut just after heading of the crop, haylage between heading and flowering, and hay just before or at the time of flowering **(Fig. 29)**. Silage and haylage will have a greater feed value than hay due to their earlier harvesting. Horses need a minimum of 30 per cent fibre in their diet to keep the gut healthy.

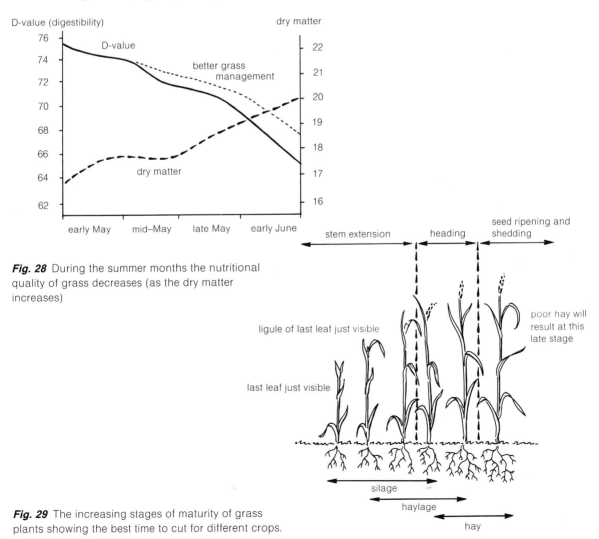

Fig. 28 During the summer months the nutritional quality of grass decreases (as the dry matter increases)

Fig. 29 The increasing stages of maturity of grass plants showing the best time to cut for different crops.

Silage

The term 'silage' includes any feedstuff which has been allowed or encouraged to pickle in its own juice. Grass and maize (corn) silage are now used extensively for horses in Europe. In the USA, silage is not normally fed to horses. However, the vacuum-packed 'Horsehage' developed in the UK is now being marketed in the USA. Silage is mostly used for feeding 'in-wintering' dairy cattle in Britain, although many horse owners are now using it, particularly when hay is scarce. Forage to be turned into silage is placed in pit/clamp silos, sealed towers or large, sealed polythene bags. The cut crop is placed directly into one of the above whilst still alive, i.e. continuing to respire and photosynthesize, and as it dies the microorganisms present on the plants begin the fermentation process, by converting nutrients in the grass. As the crop dies it is unable to make more carbohydrates through photosynthesis, but the microorganisms use up released carbohydrates from the dying plant. These are important in determining the final nutrient value of the silage, so crop death is hastened as far as possible. This is achieved by wilting the crop first, in the field, to help reduce the moisture content a little and thereby speed up the crop death process. Some of the microorganisms which are harvested with the crop are beneficial to the ensiling process, namely the lactic acid-producing bacteria. Others, such as those which produce butyric acid, are not. These bacteria give spoilt silage the rancid smell. Butyric acid-producing bacteria can only thrive in the absence of air (they are known as obligate anaerobes). Lactic acid-producing bacteria, however, can thrive with or without air (they are known as facilitative anaerobes). When the crop is initially cut there is plenty of air and so the lactic acid-producing bacteria can thrive, whereas the others cannot. As ensiling continues, the beneficial bugs have rapidly multiplied and given themselves a headstart. As fermentation continues, the amount of lactic acid produced is increased and hence the pH value drops. Most of the lactic acid production occurs after day three, and after six days the pH value should have fallen to four. This will be a well-preserved crop. If the pH value is not down to this level then the butyric acid producing-bacteria convert lactic acid to the unwanted butyric acid and start to break down the plant proteins. Some of these plant proteins will be reduced to their constituent amino acids which may then be converted by the bacteria into microbial protein. This simply means that chemical analysis of the spoilt crop will still show a relatively high crude protein analysis. Wilting also increases the concentration of the lactic acid produced (it is not as dilute) which speeds up the pickling process.

The exclusion of air in the final silage crop is vital as once air gets into the pickled crop, moulds and fungi will rapidly multiply and spoil the silage. If this happens, it should not be fed to horses under any circumstances. There is also a risk from botulism poisoning from contaminated silage. In 1994 a number of horses died from botulism after being fed big-baled silage. The offending organism *Clostridium botulinum* is present in the soil, and thrives in alkaline conditions. Thus, the pH of silage should be less than 5.5 before feeding to horses. Great care should therefore be taken when feeding big-bale, bagged silage to horses.

Fields which are to be used for a silage crop should not be grazed as dung in the resultant cut crop will spoil the ensiling process.

Haylage

Haylage is a name given to crops which are dried to 50 per cent moisture. There are several manufactures of haylage in Britain including Horsehage, Propack and Hygrass, and all seal their products in polythene bags which are small and easy to use.

Horsehage make haylage from different varieties of grass species, which means a choice for the horse owner, depending on the feed value required for individual horses, e.g. if alfalfa is used, the protein percentage will be higher than that in the ryegrass variety. Since the feed value of haylage is higher than that of hay, the manufacturers recommend that the quantity of concentrates fed should be reduced by between one half and one third. Care should be taken when feeding the high-protein varieties as they are not suitable for some horses. These products are more useful for breeding stock.

Haylage is cut at a later stage than silage and consequently has a higher percentage of dry matter. It also has a lower digestibility because there is more fibrous material in the plant stems. It is cut earlier than hay and is therefore more digestible. Fermentation of haylage is quicker than silage because it contains less moisture when cut. This means that the lactic acid is not as diluted and acts faster.

Once the sealed bag has been opened for use the haylage is exposed to air. It will therefore deteriorate quickly and should be used as soon as possible. If the bag is punctured in any way, the haylage should not be fed to horses.

Hay

As previously mentioned, the main problem with hay making used to be the dependence on the weather. If it is barn dried it can be cut at exactly the right time and the resultant crop is usually excellent in feed value. The main aim in making hay is to prevent fermentation once it has been cut. This can be guarded against by drying it as quickly as possible, bringing down the moisture content quickly to 15–20 per cent. Often, the hay is cut too late (usually because of the weather) and the resultant crop has a poor nutritional value – the lignin (indigestible fibre) level being too high and the digestibility poor. Leaf material is highest in feed value but may be lost due to shattering. This is a hazard typical of the problems associated with hay making. Hay which is cut late may have a poorer feed value than some oat or barley straw (**20a** and **b**). Meadow hay contains many different varieties of grass and it is unlikely that they will all mature at the same rate. Thus the decision as to when to harvest can be difficult.

The rapid barn-drying of hay helps to reduce the loss of β-carotene (vitamin A – see page 56), but conversely vitamin D, produced by exposure to the sun, will be in short supply. This is not, though, a good reason for not using it. Leaching may occur if the crop is rained on once it has been cut, causing the loss of soluble nutrients. These losses will be more substantial if the crop has been wilting for a couple of days before it is rained on than if it has just been cut. Rain may also encourage the growth of moulds which is certainly not desirable.

The baling of hay which is not dry enough results in the proliferation of moulds and fungi within the bale. This hay should not be used under any circumstances. This proliferation produces heat which can cause barn fires. Proper stacking minimizes the chances of this happening. When buying hay always make sure that the hay smells sweet and not musty. It is not possible to assess the nutritional quality of hay by sight and smell alone.

When hay contains timothy, if the average length of the heads is about 4.5 cm (2 in) then the hay has been cut at the right time (see **Fig. 28**). The only accurate method is to have the hay scientifically analysed. Several companies provide this service and the merchant who is supplying the hay should be able to give you a basic analysis, although as a rule they do not bother. Many yards, particularly

20 These two photographs show the difference between hay and straw
a Hay – this should be slightly green in colour and smell sweet

performance yards and studs, need to know the nutritional quality of the hay they are feeding so that they can adjust the concentrate ration accordingly. The

b Straw – the stalks are thicker and yellow in colour

variability in feed value of hay is usually determined by the stage at which it was cut (even though it may have been cured perfectly).

Finally, hay does not need to be two years old before it is fed to horses. This is a common myth amongst horse owners. After only six months' storage, the vitamin content will be almost nil and it is also far more likely to be dusty. New hay can be fed to horses once it has settled (usually about one month after storage). If it has been properly baled it should not feel warm in the centre of the bale. If it

Nutritional quality of hay

The nutritional quality of hay will be largely determined by several factors including:

- The time of cutting.
- The quality of the drying process (has it been rained on?).
- The herbage from which the hay was made.
- The soil type and fertilizer treatment.
- The number of weeds present.
- Weather conditions through the growing season.
- Method of drying, turning and baling the hay.
- Storage facilities.

does, do not use the hay. Open the new bale and introduce it slowly to the horse (as you would a new concentrate feed) to give the microorganisms in the gut time to adjust.

It is important that the horseowner does not feed any hay which contains ragwort. Once this plant has wilted with the grass it becomes more palatable to the horse. Frequently, horse owners will take a hay crop from an under-used meadow which is overgrown. These types of hay are more likely to contain weeds and ragwort and are usually poor in feed value.

Part 3
PASTURE MANAGEMENT

5

PASTURE AND ITS CONTROL

What is pasture?

Grassland management is an area which is often neglected – unsurprisingly, as it is a complex subject. However, if the pasture is carefully managed the grazing horse will benefit. All too often horses are seen grazing horse-sick, weed-infested paddocks (21). Many horse owners regard the paddock as an exercise area only, but if it is looked after properly the horse can derive most of his nutrition there, thus saving money. More importantly, a poorly managed paddock can lead to health problems, particularly if poisonous plants are present or the quality of the grazing area is poor. Grassland management includes aspects of both crop and livestock husbandry.

Pasture includes a combination of plants including grasses, clover, herbs and, all too often, weeds. There are thousands of different grasses found throughout the world and grassland comprises a large percentage of agricultural land, particularly in the UK.

There are three main types of grassland: sown leys, permanent pasture and rough grazing. Leys consist of specific mixtures of grasses and clovers which are sown to last for a limited amount of time – anything up to ten years. This is usually the case on arable farms where the fields are rotated with farm livestock. The aim is to provide top quality grassland for livestock to graze and/or for conservation, i.e. silage or hay.

Leys usually contain grasses such as timothy, meadow fescue and ryegrass together with small amounts of clovers (Fig. 30). They are not designed to meet the requirements of livestock grazing all year round and they need careful attention to remain productive (lime and fertilizers may be necessary).

Permanent pasture consists of grass which has grown naturally over many years and which may have originally been sown leys. They contain a much wider variety of grasses and plants. Native weeds and grasses can take over a sown ley relatively quickly if it is not managed properly.

When young grasses are sown they grow upright (Fig. 31), leaving patches of soil between them. These are soon filled by native grasses, providing a carpet otherwise known as the 'sward'. This carpeting is more able to withstand grazing by heavy farm livestock such as cattle or horses and reduces the likelihood of poaching (the trampling of wet fields into a quagmire), a common feature of horse pastures in the winter. The amount of grass per acre is smaller than for the sown leys but good

21 These conditions are appalling. The pasture is weed infested and loose wire and corrugated iron pose a real threat to the horse's health

timothy   perennial ryegrass   red fescue

Fig. 30 Some of the more common pasture grasses

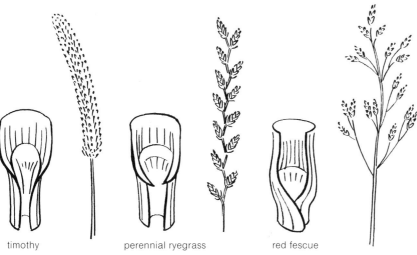

sown plants

soil level

Fig. 31 Native grasses growing between sown plants to form a sward

native grass   roots

fertilization procedures can improve grass production.

The third class of grassland is known as rough grazing and normally refers to moorland and hills where grasses have to be especially tough to be able to survive the extreme conditions. It may be used for the hardier equine breeds, such as Welsh Mountains and Shetland ponies, but finer breeds such as thoroughbreds do not suit these conditions at all. Unfortunately, rough grazing can also be applied to certain types of poor urban grassland areas which are the result of years of neglect.

Stocking rate

This refers to the amount of grassland required per horse grazing it. Obviously, this depends to a high degree on how effective the management of the pasture is. If it is poorly managed it will stock fewer horses.

The field should be divided, if at all possible, into at least three separate paddocks thus leaving at least one rested at any one time. Average grassland will support one horse per acre all year round and studs may be able to support three to four horses on 2.5 acres. The number can be increased by one third for ponies.

Practical factors to be taken into account include whether the horse is considered a 'good' or 'poor' doer. It is well known that horses and ponies differ in their efficiency at extracting nutrients from feed and conserving their energy. When two horses share the same pasture it is not uncommon for one to be overweight and the other underweight.

There is, though, no doubt that the greater the acreage per horse the easier it is to manage (within reason).

How does grass grow?

Most grasses grow as single plants and spread outwards by the growth of new shoots called tillers. These tillers grow their own branching root system **(Fig. 32)**. Some types of grass can spread across the ground by creeping stems just above or below the surface. They are beneficial in reducing damage by horse's hooves although unfortunately it is the less desirable types of grass such as bent and couch which grow in this fashion.

Normally growth begins in earnest in spring. The growing point of the plant is at ground level, at the centre of the plant, and is therefore protected, to a certain

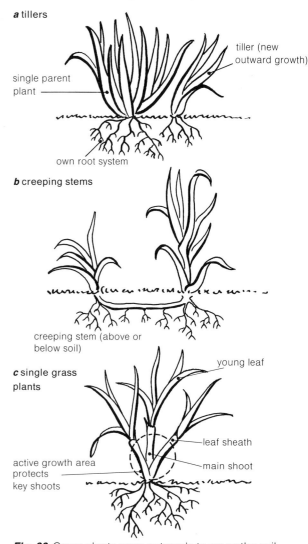

Fig. 32 Grass plants grow outwards to cover the soil area

degree, from damage by normal grazing. When stocking rates are high, horses graze closer to the ground and remove the growing point. Removal of leaves (defoliation) stimulates the growth of the grass plant and thus the sward. If the leaves are not removed by grazing or topping, i.e. the mechanical cutting of the sward, then the plant will continue to grow until it flowers.

This happens when the tillers develop into upright stalks which produce flowers. This is known as 'heading'. The flowers then produce seeds, and the stems and many of the leaves wither and die. A relatively small amount of regrowth occurs in late summer/early autumn. The amount of growth will depend upon the weather conditions **(Fig. 33)**. Late growth can provide low-quality grazing for horses over the winter months. Young spring grass contains very few stems and is therefore of good nutritional quality, containing high levels of water, protein and soluble carbohydrates. Because there are fewer stems the fibre level is low. As the grass grows throughout the spring and summer and heading occurs, the nutritional quality reduces correspondingly. The grass becomes higher in fibre (more woody) and lower in protein, soluble carbohydrates and water.

To summarize, the pattern of grass growth involves a peak in spring and a smaller peak in autumn. It is important that horse owners are aware of this pattern of grass growth as careful management can reduce the incidence of laminitis. Also, the feeding of concentrates (if they are being fed at all) should be adjusted to take into account the nutrition from the grass.

Clovers, unlike grasses, have special nodules on their roots containing bacteria **(Fig. 34)** and as such are classified as legumes. The bacteria take nitrogen from the air (known as 'nitrogen fixing') and convert it to useful forms of nitrates, and

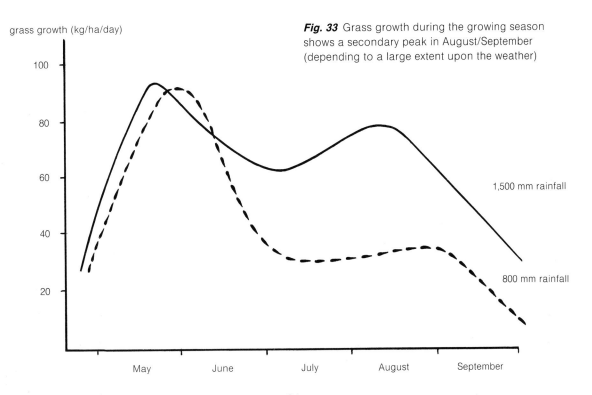

grass growth (kg/ha/day)

Fig. 33 Grass growth during the growing season shows a secondary peak in August/September (depending to a large extent upon the weather)

1,500 mm rainfall

800 mm rainfall

May   June   July   August   September

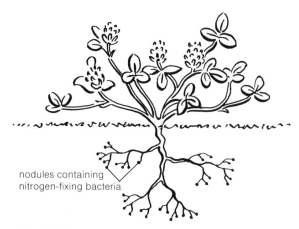

Fig. 34 Clover is a legume and this diagram shows the important root nodules which contain the nitrogen-fixing bacteria

nodules containing nitrogen-fixing bacteria

eventually valuable proteins. Nitrogen is also released into the soil when the nodules fall off and it can then be used by neighbouring grass plants. Too much clover in the sward can lead to problems due to excessive nitrogen levels, but small amounts are beneficial **(22)**.

Weeds thrive on bare patches, poached areas or sour areas. The seeds of weeds are opportunist and will grow wherever they can. They are not deterred by poor conditions and species such as buttercups, nettles, thistles, ragwort, St John's wort, docks and plantains are a common sight. Weeds are normally relatively unpalat-able, but if the grass plants are grazed heavily weeds take over, sometimes with fatal consequences.

There is no doubt that newly sown, highly fertilized leys and some permanent pastures are too rich for many horses, particularly barren mares, resting horses, native ponies, some youngstock and even pregnant mares. Grazing horses on these pastures can lead to problems such as obesity, laminitis and developmental problems such as DOD. A balance needs to be achieved whereby the pasture is neither too rich nor too poor. This is often quite difficult to achieve.

When looking for grasses to use for horse pastures there are various criteria which should be met if possible:

- It should be palatable and be able to withstand fairly intensive grazing and cutting.
- It should be resistant to disease.
- It is preferable to choose species with different flowering times over the summer period to ensure an even spread of grass growth.

22 Clover can be a valuable protein source to grazing horses, but too much may cause problems

- It should be able to withstand the winter weather even though growth during this time will be slow, if any.
- It should provide an even carpet or sward over the soil. This will reduce cutting but it will also help to cushion the effects of galloping horses (especially youngstock) and help protect their joints from injury.

Varieties of grass

The different properties of grasses are instrumental in the decision making process of sowing a pasture:

- Perennial ryegrass – versatile, very persistent in good rich soil but does well in all types of soil.
- Crested dog's tail – very palatable to horses.
- Creeping red fescue – thrives under difficult conditions, palatable, good nutritional quality.
- Smooth stalked meadow grass – (Kentucky blue grass) suits light sandy soils.
- Rough stalked meadow grass – suits moist rich soils, palatable, has a good carpeting effect.
- Wild white clover – withstands drought and enhanced soil nitrogen levels. Avoid excessive amounts.

A good mix for a pasture for horses would therefore be as follows:

- Two perennial ryegrasses – 50 per cent.
- Two creeping red fescues – 25 per cent.
- Rough or smooth stalked meadow grass – 5–10 per cent.
- Crested dogs tail – 5–10 per cent.
- Wild white clover – 1–2 per cent.

Fertilizers

All grass will need fertilizing from time to time and applying the correct amount of the required fertilizer will enhance grass growth and keep the sward healthy. Even on thoroughbred studs, care should be taken not to over fertilize. Many horse pastures never see an ounce of fertilizer, whereas others are treated like those required for intensive dairy farming.

Pastures need to be fertilized as nutrients are removed from the soil when the grass is eaten. Much attention is paid to the major nutrients such as nitrogen (N), phosphorous (P), potassium (K), calcium (Ca), magnesium (Mg) and sometimes salt (NaCl). However, rarely is enough attention paid to the trace minerals in the soil which may be deficient, or may be present in such levels that they effectively 'lockup' other trace minerals. For example, if the molybdenum level is too high, it will reduce the availability of copper. This can have disastrous consequences on fast-growing youngstock. Levels of trace minerals are to some extent determined by the soil and rock types but may be affected by industrial pollution. Where the soil is sandy, these trace minerals are more likely to be leached out.

Procedures followed by farmers for dairy pastures should certainly not be used for horses. Fertilizer bags have figures on them, such as 20:10:10. This refers to the NPK levels (nitrogen, phosphorous and potassium). The fertilizer in this example therefore contains 20 units of nitrogen (N_2), 10 units of phosphate (P_2O_5) and 10 units of potash (K_2O).

Soil should be tested on a fairly regular basis – once every three years is about right. This will pick up any deficiencies and give the pH level of the soil. Most soils in the UK are naturally acidic, often with a pH level of 5.5 or less. In the US one should check with a county extension agent. The pH for optimum grass growth is 6.8 (lime is used to increase the pH).

There are several different types of fertilizer available, both organic and inorganic. The former are derived from substances produced by living organisms such as seaweed and manure, and the latter are of mineral origin, such as limestone, nitrate and phosphate of potash.

The inorganic fertilizers contain just a few compounds, and are released rapidly into the soil where they are quickly taken up by the plant. They are the more likely to be leached out of the soil. Nitrates in particular can speedily induce lush grass growth which may be too much for the grazing horse.

Organic fertilizers are more complicated and contain a much wider range of compounds and nutrients, including trace minerals. They can also include such matter as rotting straw from farmyard manure, which improves the soil structure. Organic fertilizers take much longer to break down into the soil and can be termed 'slow-release'. Pastures should be rested until the cattle manure has rotted well into the soil. Poultry manure should be avoided because of the high nitrogen content, and pig manure because it may be too high in copper. Human sewage may introduce harmful heavy metals into the soil and should also be avoided). Many companies now manufacture organic and 'semi-organic' (mixtures of organic and inorganic) fertilizers which are extremely useful.

Seaweed based fertilizers are proving popular. They are easy to use and come in suitable quantities for small horse paddocks. Care should be taken not to overuse them as iodine levels may become too high. If a calcified seaweed fertilizer is used then there is no need to lime the pasture as well (see the ADAS soil fertility scale table). Where the index value is two or above then no fertilizer is required for that particular nutrient at that time.

Lime

As previously stated, the ideal pH for soil is 6.8. This implies a high availability of

ADAS soil fertility scale

Index Number	P	K (mg/litre of soil)	Mg
0	0–9	0–60	0–25
1	10–15	61–120	26–50
2	16–25	121–240	51–100
3	26–45	241–400	101–175
4	46–70	401–600	176–250
5	71–100	601–900	251–350

calcium which is beneficial to growing youngstock. If the soil is tested and proves too acidic then lime should be added in the form of ground limestone or pit chalk. If the pH is too high and the soil too alkaline essential minerals will be locked up. Although difficult to correct, it can sometimes be done using an application of sulphate of ammonia.

Phosphorous

It is essential to keep a correct balance of calcium to phosphorous for bone growth and development. If the index is one or low two then basic slag can be added (9–22 per cent phosphate). This is a by-product of steel production. The phosphate is released slowly and gently and should be applied every two to three years.

Potassium

Large amounts of nitrogen will make the soil bitter and potassium can be used as a grass sweetener. An index of one to two is sufficient. Potassium may be needed if grass is being grown for hay or silage.

Nitrogen

The use of nitrogen on pastures for horses is contentious, although it is agreed that some is needed. Too much nitrogen leads to overly lush grass, and problems. No more than 30 units should be used for equine pastures, but this can be increased for a hay crop.

Magnesium

If the magnesium level is very low then it will lock up calcium, copper and sulphur. This is not desirable. Magnesium can be added to fertilizers, and if the soil is acidic magnesium limestone can be used. This problem generally occurs in lighter soils.

Trace minerals

Pasture requirements of trace elements is a complicated subject. In the past, the use of slow-releasing organic fertilizers containing variable amounts of trace elements prevented true deficiencies. Also, land was less intensively grazed as there was more of it available. Clay soils which have fewer problems with leaching are normally richer in trace elements, while sandy ones are more likely to be deficient.

The availability of trace minerals is defined by geographical location. For example, in the UK, magnesium, copper and iodine may be deficient in the Cotswolds or the chalk downlands. Copper deficiency may also be a problem in parts of Somerset and Eire. Alkaline soils tend to lock-up manganese and copper so grass levels will give false readings as to the soil levels. Selenium deficiency in the soil is known to be prevalent in the Scottish Highlands, Shropshire and parts of Cornwall, and in the US 40 states are known to have areas that are deficient. This is most prevalent in acid soils. The US also contains areas where levels of selenium are toxic.

Iodine may be present in excess in coastal areas, and the use of iodized salt, seaweed supplements and fertilizers should be avoided in such places. Iodine is deficient in areas of Derbyshire in the UK, Colorado, California, Illinois, North and South Dakota, New York, Nebraska, Ohio, Oregon, Utah and Washington in the US. Here, iodized salt should be fed and the use of seaweed based supplements may be beneficial. Both iodine deficiency and toxicity produce goitre (an enlarged thyroid gland). This can have drastic effects on youngstock and can affect the foetus of pregnant mares.

The widespread application of trace minerals to the soil is not a good idea as problems may be created with trace mineral interactions. Also, the uptake of these minerals may be limited and so expensive repeated applications may be necessary. In my experience the use of good organic fertilizers and supplementary feeding of trace elements in known deficient areas is the most practical solution.

The initial application of fertilizer, whichever one you are using, should be made in about mid-March or as soon as spring growth commences. ADAS (in the UK) will be able to give advice on soil testing, the use of fertilizers and their application in known deficient areas as they now employ equine specialists. In the US, ask your county extension agent. Soil testing should be carried out approximately every three years, and samples should be taken from both roughs and lawns. Roughs tend to be higher in potash.

The control of weeds

Weeds reduce the nutritional quality of the pasture and some may also be poisonous. They compete with grass plants for space and nourishment, therefore reducing the quantity of grass available to the horse **(23)**. The most common weeds that affect pastures in the UK are:

- nettle
- dock
- buttercup
- ragwort
- creeping thistle
- spear thistle
- chickweed
- foxglove
- rush horsetail
- St John's wort
- broad-leaved plantain

There are two main methods of weed control – chemical and physical.

Chemical control

This involves the use of herbicides (weed killers). Spraying from a tractor is a quick and effective method of weed control. It also enables the farmer to reach otherwise inaccessible areas, such as underneath fences and around the base of trees. It is an economical and labour-saving method of weed removal. Mowing or topping of the pasture (see physical control) will not cut the low-growing weeds but chemicals have the advantage of being able to root them out.

Spraying may need to be carried out twice a year and the pasture should be rested afterwards, for approximately two weeks (see manufacturer's instructions). Herbicides are most effective if used when the weed is in its rapid-growth phase. An alternative for smaller areas is spot spraying. This involves someone walking around the pasture with a knapsack-type spray unit attacking individual weeds.

Use a herbicide which will not kill the clover, unless the particular pasture contains an excess. Always follow the manufacturers instructions.

Physical control

Mowing or topping using a tractor-

23 Nettles are a common weed, especially in horse-sick pastures

mounted mower should be done about four times during the season. Once cut, the weeds and cut grass need to be removed or they will prevent the growth of new grass underneath. If it is not, you will see that the grass below will go yellow after only a couple of weeks. Another reason for clearing is that poisonous plants, such as ragwort, are more palatable to the horse once dead.

Topping is beneficial in that it encourages tillering and the production of more of the nutritious leaves. It will also prevent the pasture 'going to seed' as it delays the flowering (heading) process.

With some weeds, the only effective method of control is removal by hand, and this is certainly the case for ragwort. This job is better done after it has rained and the soil is looser. Pulled plants should be removed and burnt, and any new plants should be removed immediately. The presence of ragwort in pastures for horses is extremely common, but by ignoring it horse owners take a potentially fatal risk.

It is important to horse owners in the UK that they are aware of the Injurious Weeds Order. This permits the serving on the occupier of any land a notice to destroy certain injurious weeds. These include creeping and spear thistle, curled and broad-leaved dock, and ragwort.

Poisonous pasture plants

Unfortunately, a large number of plants are poisonous to the grazing horse. Their effects vary and while some can be fatal when only very small quantities are consumed, others have a cumulative effect. Some poisons may be ingested without clinical symptoms appearing, but the horse may undergo changes in temperament, fitness and loss of resistance to disease.

Horsetails or mare's-tails have a cumulative effect and the poison, called thiami-nase, acts by destroying vitamin B_1 (thiamin). Bracken also contains thiaminase – it is very common on higher ground, i.e. hill areas where grass is often in short supply and, therefore, horses will eat it **(24)**.

Other plants can cause allergic reactions, such as nettles, which may produce nettle rash (*urticaria*) when the horse's skin comes into contact with them. St John's wort, when ingested, can at certain times in its growth cause fairly severe photosensitization.

In the US there are a vast number of poisonous plants. Many species have several names which makes identification on a standard basis difficult. Chokecherry is a plant found lining many fence rows in the US that contains a cyanide-forming glycoside poison. The effects of this poison take place very quickly (within minutes) and the horse will be in great distress before (due to lack of oxygen) convulsing, becoming comatose and dying. Unfortunately, horses will eat this plant if it has wilted. Although the condition is treatable, help may not be found in time.

24 Bracken contains an enzyme called thiaminase which may lead to a deficiency of vitamin B_1 (thiamin)

Other problem plants in the US include white snakeroot, Russian knapweed and yellow star thistle. Horses will actually seek these plants out. The latter two plants need to be ingested in large amounts before toxicity symptoms occur. Once they do, the poison destroys the part of the brain which controls the chewing mechanism.

Crazyweed, or locoweed, can be addictive to horses who seem to crave this poisonous plant. The poison contains a substance which destroys nerve cells in the brain and eyes. The effects are irreversible. The horse loses his sense of spatial awareness and cannot judge sizes or distances of objects, overcompensating in his behaviour as a result. He will walk into fences and other objects. Affected horses are a danger to themselves and their owners and are usually destroyed.

Horses are most at risk when grazing is in short supply, but an equally disturbing hazard occurs in urban areas where local gardeners use the pasture as a tip for gardening waste.

Ragwort

Ragwort (*Senecio jacobaea*) is probably the most common culprit of poisoning in Britain. In one incident, five horses out of a group of 20 died after feeding on the weed. The characteristic yellow-flowered plants are unfortunately a very common sight on many equine pastures **(25)**. The poison is a Pyrrolizidine alkaloid which causes cumulative liver damage. Because the effects build up slowly they may not be noticed until a few weeks after the horse has been eating the ragwort. Symptoms of poisoning include weight loss, anorexia, depression, yawning, colic, head-pressing against fixed objects, aimless walking and circling, jaundice, oedema and incoordination. The horse will eventually die. If the liver is badly damaged then prognosis

25 Ragwort is probably the most common cause of horse poisoning in the UK

is guarded as there is no treatment, although therapy can be given to prevent the damaged liver 'overworking'. This includes a low-protein, high-energy diet, glucose, B-vitamins, antibiotics and careful nursing with rest.

In the case of ragwort, prevention is certainly better than cure. Remove all the plants from the pasture. Be vigilant for the presence of ragwort in hay which has been bought in. Once the plant has died it becomes more palatable to the horse. It can also become palatable following treatment with a selective weed killer.

Other plants that cause a similar liver condition include heliotrope and the legume crotalaria, numerous species of which have proved their toxicity to horses in the US, Australia and South Africa. One species of this legume causes a disease called Kimberley horse disease.

Yew

The yew is extremely poisonous, the most poisonous plant in Britain, and even one mouthful can be fatal. The poison is the alkaloid taxine, which affects the heart. Signs of poisoning are quick to reveal themselves and the horse usually dies within five minutes. Symptoms include staggering, convulsions, collapse, difficulty in breathing and death from heart failure. There is no treatment and so any offending yew should be fenced off or cut down.

Oak

Oak leaves and acorns contain a poisonous substance called tannic acid. Many horses like to eat acorns and will actively search then out. The poison causes kidney damage and gastroenteritis, and symptoms include anorexia, colic and constipation followed by diarrhoea, which is often bloodstained. There may also be blood in the urine.

Again, there is no treatment and the oak trees should be fenced off. Offending acorns should be removed from the pasture. Horses die from acorn poisoning every autumn and so the presence of oak trees and acorns must be taken seriously.

Trees that are safe around horse pastures include scots pine, willow, white pine, sycamore, red pine and white cedar.

Many leguminous plants contain a variety of poisons, such as laburnum, broom and lupin. In the case of lupins it is the seed which contains the poison and on occasion horses that have eaten lupin seeds have died from respiratory paralysis. The chronic liver damage associated with lupinosis in horses is caused by a fungus growing on the plant.

Some of the pasture legumes such as subterranean clover (*Trifolium subterraneum*) that grow on light soils contain appreciable amounts of hormones called oestrogens. These can affect fertility although the true effect on breeding mares is not known.

Sweet clover contains coumarin which is broken down chemically to dicoumarol in hay which has not dried properly during harvesting. Under these conditions moulds may form. Dicoumarol prolongs blood clotting time, thus this hay should not be used for horses. Poisonous bulbs include daffodil, snowdrop, hyacinth and bluebell.

Any known poisonous plants should be removed from the pasture and, even if they taste bitter, it is simply not worth the risk of leaving them there in the hope that this will be a deterrent.

Poisonous plants found in Britain

alder buckthorne
black bryany
black nightshade
bog asphodel
bracket
broom
buckthorn
chickweed
columbine
corncockle
cowbane
darnel
deadly nightshade
flax
foxglove
fritillaria
greater columbine
hellebore
hemlock
hemlock water dropwort
hemp
henbane
herb Paris
horsetail
iris
laburnum
larkspur
laurel
lily of the valley
lupin
meadow saffron
monkshood
oak (acorns)
pimpernel
poppy
potato
privet
ragwort
rhododendron
sandwort
scapwort
sowbread
St John's wort
thornapple
white bryony

Poisonous plants found in the US

bitterweed (sneezeweed)
black snakeroot
black locust
bracken
buckeye
Carolina jessamine
climbing bittersweet
dogbone
ivy
jinson weed
laurel
locoweed
lupines
milkweed
nightshade
oak (acorns)
poison hemlock
pokeweed
rattle box
water hemlock
white snake root
wild cherry trees
wild tobacco

Note In the US the County Agent or Farm Advisor will have a list of the poisonous plants in their area.

6
PRACTICAL MANAGEMENT

6

PRACTICAL MANAGEMENT

Rolling

Most damage to pastures takes place in wet weather. Winter poaching will make the field very uneven in the spring and summer as the ground dries out. Rolling helps flatten the ground and irons out the uneven areas. It also pushes loose stones back into the soil. Tillering is encouraged as the crushed plant produces secondary growth points and thus increases the nutritious leaf content of the sward.

If the pasture is rolled after a top dressing of fertilizer it will help to incorporate the granules into the soil. Pasture should be rolled in March/April, when it is suitably dry.

Harrowing

Harrowing usefully removes the dead grass from the sward although it also spreads manure, and therefore worm larvae, around the pasture (26). Hot, dry conditions are the best for harrowing, as they kill the worm larvae, although the end of the season (October/November) is not a bad time. It is a good idea to rest the pasture after harrowing for a few weeks.

Renovation of pasture

Generally speaking, there is little advantage in ploughing up poor pasture unless the owner is prepared to grow an arable crop for at least three to four years. Ploughing should only be a last resort. The alternative, upgrading, is not just a short-term measure. Once the pasture has been renovated it will still require regular management, so the soil and drainage should be basically sound before any attempts at improvement are made. If they are not, the grass will simply deteriorate again.

To improve a pasture it must first be topped and then allowed to rest and regrow (this will naturally include weeds). A suitable herbicide can then be applied and after a couple of weeks the fields should be harrowed and fertilized. If bare patches are exposed where weeds grew previously, then suitable varieties of grass seed may be scattered. A heavy roller will help to push them into the soil. The pasture should not be grazed until these new areas are well established, and it may need topping again to promote tillering. Although the upgrading of pasture may be a relatively expensive exercise, it is important to remember that good grass can provide all the nutrients that the horse needs and if it is well looked after the amount of supplementary feed required will be dramatically reduced.

Fig. 35 shows roughly when to carry out certain management procedures on paddocks.

26 Harrowing should be carried out in hot, dry
conditions

27 Horses may be grazed with cattle to break the life
cycle of worms. They also graze areas of pasture
which horses may leave

How to guard against an unhealthy pasture

- If possible, collect the droppings regularly and frequently.
- Rest each paddock for at least three months in the rotation cycle to allow the sward to recover.
- If possible, rotate with cattle as this helps to prevent the separation of pastures into very short lawns and very long roughs. Either graze the horses first, or simultaneously, with the cattle. Cattle break the worm life cycles and therefore help in worm control **(27)**.
- After the cattle and/or horses have been moved off the pasture, top if necessary, harrow and rest.
- The grass should not be allowed to grow longer than 4–6 in (10–15 cm) high at any time. This prevents flowering and the grass going to seed.
- The best way to cure horse-sick pasture is to rest it completely, fertilize and kill any weeds before taking a couple of hay crops. Ideally, every paddock should have a complete rest from horses every fifth year, but this is usually not practical.

Drainage

Pastures which are known to be wet, for example those where rushes and marsh grasses grow in abundance, should be avoided at all costs. In the winter they turn into bogs and in the summer the wet areas are breeding grounds for flies **(28)**. Boggy ground will also prevent the growth of good grass and herbage as the roots are starved of oxygen. If the land is particularly bad it may be worth having a drainage system installed. This can be expensive but the drains last a long time.

Some pastures have natural drainage in the form of a gentle slope with a river or brook running at the bottom. These can be useful for horses. Steep slopes are not suitable unless there are flat areas where the horses can rest. Ponies which are used to these extreme conditions do adapt to suit the environment.

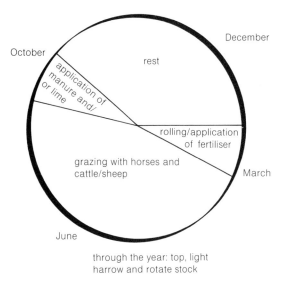

December

October

application of manure and/or lime

rest

rolling/application of fertiliser

grazing with horses and cattle/sheep

March

June

through the year: top, light harrow and rotate stock

Fig. 35 Management procedures of pasture throughout the year

28 Horses are renowned for 'poaching' pastures, particularly by the gates where they will often congregate

29 Good hedges should be about 5 ft (1.5 m) high and thick enough to prevent horses going through them

Hedges and trees

Hedges and trees may have been planted or grown up naturally. They provide natural windbreaks and shelters. Big old trees, if they have good thick canopies, will also provide protection against rain when horses stand underneath them. Hedges should ideally be about 1.5 m (5 ft) high **(29)** and not be allowed to become thin, letting horses through. Once the hedge has been properly laid it should be cut regularly. To be on the safe side it is often prudent to line hedges with other fencing. Ditches should also be fenced off so that animals, particularly foals, do not roll into them. With regard to trees, care should be taken to ensure that they are not poisonous, for example oak trees should be fenced off so that the acorns do not fall on to the pasture.

Fencing

When considering which types of fencing to use there are certain important considerations. Firstly, fencing should be safe and secure: it should not be able to cause injury to the horses enclosed in it, and it should prevent horses escaping from it; it must be low enough to prevent horses and ponies rolling under it, and high enough to prevent the more athletic horses jumping over it.

Post and rail fencing Post and rail fencing is without doubt the safest type of fencing. It is secure and the rails can be placed at the correct heights. Three or two rails can be used depending upon the final height required **(30)**. The upper rail should

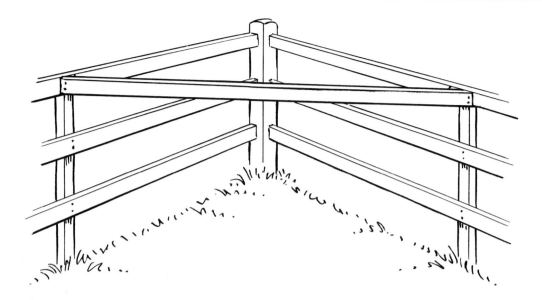

not be below the top of the post because if the post juts out it may cause injuries. Fences are usually made from wood and should be creosoted to prevent weather damage and horses chewing it. Pipe fencing may be used on a post and rail system. This is safe but can be expensive to maintain.

Stud rails Stud rails are safe and durable. They consist of solid plastic strips about 10 cms (4 ins) wide incorporating high-tensile wire. The strips come in rolls and are used in two or three rows of rail.

Plastic fencing is now very popular. It obviously has a longer lifespan than wooden fencing and is easier to maintain. The posts may be made from wood or plastic. Flexafence, a British product, consists of straps of treated nylon webbing covered with PVC and nailed to wooden posts.

Wire fencing If wire fencing is to be used then a top rail must also be built in to prevent horses running into it.

Woven V-mesh wire is safe for horses because the holes are too small to allow a hoof through. However, sheep netting (often seen lining horse paddocks) is cer-

Fig. 36 Fencing off sharp corners with a rail will help to reduce the risk of accidents

tainly not recommended as squares are large enough for hooves to slip through and horrific injuries to the foot, particularly the pastern and heel, can result. I have removed a shire horse from sheep netting who had managed to put both front feet through the wire and cutters were needed to set him free.

Care should be taken to ensure that fencing is never slack. Injuries with plain wire can be worse than those caused by barbed wire.

Barbed wire fencing Horses and barbed wire really do not mix under any circumstances. Even when placed along the top rail of post and rail fencing, horses can still catch themselves on it, and eye injuries can be inflicted by horses scratching their heads on the fence. Loose and rusty barbed-wire fences are often seen enclosing horses and it is simply a matter

30 A good example of post and rail fencing with natural shelter provided by the tree

of time before serious injuries result **(32)**. Many horse owners believe that horses 'respect' barbed wire: this is simply not true. Do not take the risk.

Electric fencing This has to be used extremely carefully: horses do not always see a single strand of electric wire across their paddock. There are now types of electric fencing which are much more visible to the horse **(31)**: some are reflective and others, such as meshed electric fencing (widely used in the US), are brightly coloured so that horses can easily see it.

Many horse owners use a single strand of electric fencing along the top of the post and rail to keep horses away from the fence. This seems to work quite well as long as the electric wire is positioned so that playful youngstock cannot get their feet caught between the upper rail and the wire.

Horses should be introduced to the electric fence carefully, with the horse owner leading the horse on a headcollar to the fence. Once the horse has received a small shock then he should stay away from the fence.

Gates Gates, like fences, should be safe and secure **(33)**. Horses tend to congregate

32 Loose and rusty barbed wire is extremely dangerous to horses

around gateways, particularly at feeding time, and the area can become severely poached. Stone chippings, sand, cinders or fine shale (not rubble and bricks) can be put down to keep the area drained. The gateway should preferably be dug out first and the chosen material added afterwards. Wood shavings and straw are not a good choice as they tend to get poached in as well.

31 This electric fencing is easily visible to the horse and when applied above post and rail is very effective

33 Fence gates must be both safe and secure

Gates should have secure locks or bolts on them, ones which playful horses cannot undo by themselves! Traditional five-bar gates made from wood or tubular metal are the most popular (**Fig. 37**) and should be hung so that there is no chance of the horses getting their feet caught underneath. The gate should swing freely so that the horse owner should not have to lift it to move it. The hanging posts need to be substantial, such as old telegraph poles or railway sleepers, and should be set in concrete. Many accidents have been caused by over-eager horses barging through gates which the horse owner is still attempting to open.

Field shelters

Shelter from trees and hedges may not always be sufficient in extreme weather conditions for the finer breeds of horse. A well-built field shelter will encourage horses to use it if it is light and airy, so the opening should be wide or open-fronted to prevent horses becoming trapped inside (**34**). A gate may be attached so that a horse may be enclosed if necessary. If bedding is to be used then the shelter should be on a hard-standing (concrete) base or the area will become soiled and poached.

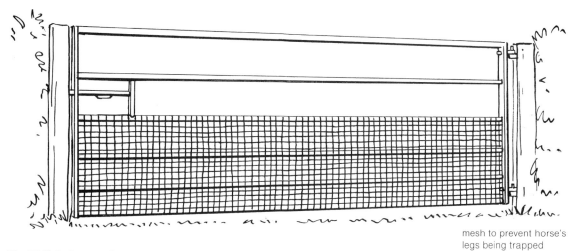

mesh to prevent horse's
legs being trapped

Fig. 37 Tubular metal gate

34 A well-constructed field shelter

35 Two types of water trough
a This is self-filling and positioned between two fields.

The field shelter should be sited either well away from the fence or directly against it. The back of the shelter should be againt the prevailing wind. Shelters vary in size from a basic pony shelter, 3 m × 3 m (10 ft × 10 ft), to 18 m × 12 m (60 ft × 40 ft) for several horses. They can be particularly useful in the summer months as flies tend to stay outside.

Water sources

Streams should be running with a solid bottom; preferably not clay or sandy or the horse may develop sand colic. They should be clean and pollution free, and stagnant ponds should be avoided at all costs. If the horse owner is not sure about the quality of the water the National Rivers Authority (UK), or another appropriate authority, should be asked to analyse it.

Horses confined in paddocks must have access to clean fresh water on a 24 hour basis. Running, piped water to self-filling troughs is the ideal situation **(35a** and **b)**. These can be purchased from agricultural suppliers. If a ballcock is used it should be out of reach of the horses as they do like to chew them! Troughs should be regularly cleaned and checked and care taken that they are not placed under deciduous trees.

b This water trough has sharp edges, is not self-filling and the hedge overhangs it so that leaves may drop into the water and contaminate it

In the winter the water may freeze. This has to be thawed so that horses still have a water supply.

Feeding equipment

Care must be taken when feeding horses at grass, especially when several horses share the same pasture, which is common. They will fight over concentrates and hay and, for this reason, they should if possible all be fed at the same time. If not, they should be brought in from the field and fed away from the others. In the US many yards use long troughs for feeding, but care should be taken to ensure there is plenty of space per horse.

When feeding hay it can be laid out on the ground providing it is not too wet, and each pile should be at least 4 m (12 ft) away from the next. If hay nets are used they must be high enough to prevent the horse getting his feet ensnared. Hay racks should also be designed to avoid the same hazard, and also so as not to pull hay into their eyes. There should be no sharp projections.

Plastic feed mangers are available which simply hook over the top rail of post and rail fencing. Several of these could be used along a fence to keep horses apart whilst they are feeding.

Part 4
HEALTH
AND
DISEASE

7

DISEASE
AND
PREVENTION

Recognizing signs of good and ill health

It is important to know when a horse is showing signs of ill health and when it is serious enough to warrant the attention of the veterinary surgeon. Simple health checks and first-aid measures can help enormously, so horse owners ought to be able to take the horse's temperature, pulse and respiratory rate. They should also be competent at treating simple wounds and injuries, and understand the importance of nursing the horse back to full health. Knowledge of emergency first aid may prevent the horse suffering further trauma and may improve the chances of a quick and full recovery. This in turn will give the owner more confidence and prevent panic. It is also important that the administration of certain drugs and medicines including wormers can be undertaken with the minimum of fuss.

Many horse owners develop a sixth sense and instinctively know when all is not well with horses in their care.

Temperature

The horse's normal body temperature is 38°C (100.5°F). This can vary by half a degree between individual horses and at different times of the day. Foals have a higher 'normal' temperature of 38.6°C (101.5°F). Fevers and infections tend to raise the temperature as the body's defence mechanism tries to fight off the invading viruses or bacteria. Shock, on the other hand, can lower the temperature.

If the adult horse's temperature goes above 38.6°C (101.5°F) or below 37°C (100°F) the veterinary surgeon should be called.

The temperature should be taken with either a clinical mercury thermometer or a digital one – in my view digital thermometers are safer. The horse should be kept quiet and may need to be restrained. The tail should be gently lifted to allow access to the anus, the thermometer lubricated with petroleum jelly, and inserted into the horses rectum (36). A mercury thermometer needs to be left in place for about one minute, and a digital thermometer will beep three times when the temperature is known. It is vital that the thermometer is held firmly at all times. Make sure that the thermometer is thoroughly cleaned in disinfectant and rinsed before it is returned to its case.

Respiratory rate (breathing rate)

It is fairly simple to watch a horse breathing and count the number of breaths per minute; the horse at rest normally takes in air about eight to twelve times per minute. An increased respiratory rate will occur if the horse has a fever, and is also a symptom of pneumonia or pleurisy. Exercise and excitement also increase the breathing rate so don't measure it in these conditions.

Horses who have chronic obstructive pulmonary disease (COPD) need an extra effort to expel air from the lungs. This is manifested as the characteristic double lift of the ribcage as air is forced out of the lungs.

Pulse rate (heart rate)

The normal resting pulse of the horse is 30–40 beats per minute. This increases with exercise, excitement, pain or when the horse has a temperature.

The easiest place to take the pulse is where the facial artery passes under the lower jaw (37). Run your hands along the lower jaw and you will feel a pulsing tube when light pressure is applied. Count the number of beats over 15 seconds and then multiply this number by four to obtain the pulse rate per minute.

Knowing the pulse rate is an important method of checking the fitness level after work (particularly endurance work).

Signs of health

If the horse owner is aware of the signs of good health, any problems will be more easily detected. The signs of a healthy horse (38) include:

- Good appetite
- Bright alert attitude
- Glossy healthy skin and coat
- Bright eyes
- Clean nostrils
- Droppings should be passed regularly and break on hitting the ground. They should be pale to dark brown, not black
- Condition should be optimal, not over or under weight
- Posture and behaviour (should not be lying down excessively)

Normal TPR = Temperature: 38°C (100.5°F)
Pulse: 30–40 beats per minute
Respiratory rate: 8–12 breaths per minute.

The importance of vaccination

Vaccination is a form of preventitive medicine which is carried out to help keep the horse in good health. The most commonly used vaccines, for the majority of the equine population, are those against tetanus and equine influenza.

A vaccine is a solution which contains live, altered or killed microorganisms (bacteria or viruses), or the part of the microorganism which stimulates immunity to the particular bug. The influenza vaccine, for example, contains several strains of killed flu viruses.

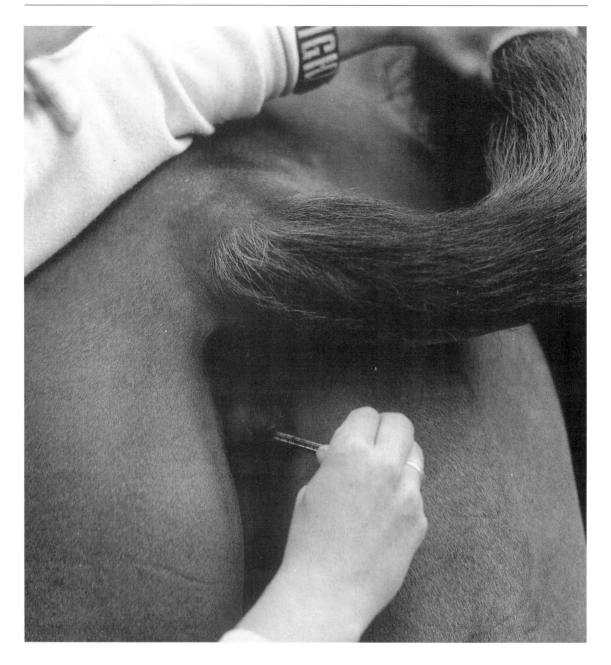

36 Taking the horse's temperature rectally, with a clinical thermometer

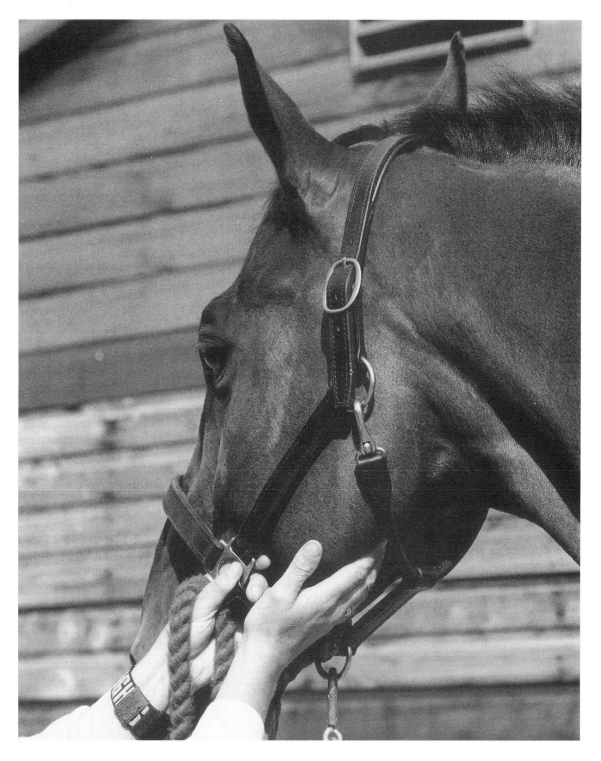

37 Taking the horse's pulse

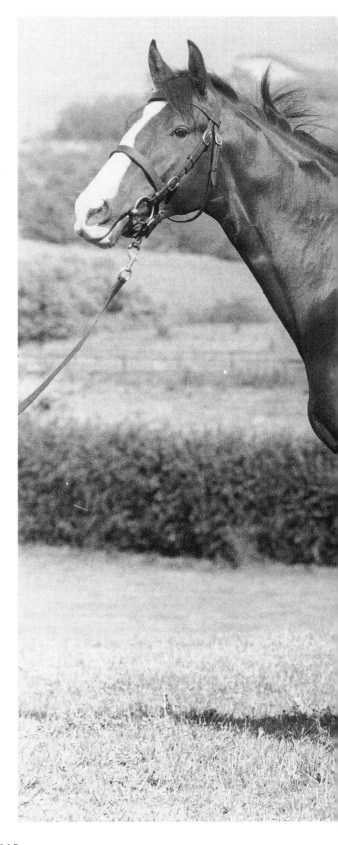

38 The picture of good health with a gleaming coat and bright eye

Equine influenza

A highly infectious viral disease which may seriously affect the horse's health in both the short and long term. Permanent damage to the lungs and heart can result in long-term problems such as susceptibility to future secondary infections. Different strains and sub-types of the equine flu virus exist and these have been named after the places where they were first isolated, e.g. Miami, Kentucky, Fontainebleau. The viruses which cause equine flu are split into two groups A/Equi 1 and A/Equi 2.

There is a worldwide distribution of flu viruses and serious outbreaks of flu flare up every few years resulting in epidemics.

Symptoms

A harsh, dry cough which can spread rapidly amongst all the horses at grass if they have not been vaccinated. Those infected develop a high temperature (41°C/ 106°F), loss of appetite and depression. A watery discharge from the nose may become thick, yellow and pus-like. The horse may also be stiff and constipated.

The illness usually lasts for about two weeks but complications such as pleurisy, pneumonia and/or damage to the heart may follow. Foals are particularly susceptible to influenza, and they may die of pneumonia.

The disease is spread by coughing which throws the viruses into the air. They are then inhaled by other horses.

Treatment

There is no method for treating the virus once it has taken hold. Horses must be rested and nursed back to health. They should be kept warm but also have plenty of fresh air as a dust free environment will reduce the risk of further, secondary bacterial infections.

Prevention is undoubtedly better than cure. Vaccinated horses may contract the disease as immunity is not 100 per cent guaranteed, but the symptoms they suffer are much milder.

Vaccination

Vaccination should be carried out at three months of age. All vaccination programmes require two initial doses within an interval of four to six weeks, followed by a third injection six months later. Thereafter, boosters should be given at intervals of no longer than 12 months. In an effort to reduce outbreaks, many organizers of equine competitions now require all entrants to be vaccinated (up to date) against flu. These include the Jockey Club, FEI (Federation Equestre Internationale) and the BHS (British Horse Society).

Tetanus

Tetanus is caused by a toxin produced by the bacterium *Clostridium tetani*. Of all the domestic animals, horses are the most susceptible. The bacterium is most commonly found in the soil and is also a normal inhabitant of the digestive tract. Tetanus occurs in all parts of the world, and certain localities are known to be high risk areas. It is usually seen in isolated cases and infection results in a high mortality rate (90 per cent). The organism enters through puncture wounds (particularly in the foot), the umbilicus of the newborn foal, or via the digestive tract.

Symptoms

The incubation period varies between one and three weeks although it may be much longer.

The initial signs are progressive muscle stiffness accompanied by spasms and paralysis, and soon jaw movement becomes restricted, hence the term 'lockjaw'. All four limbs are stiff and the horse adopts a characteristic 'saw-horse' posture with his tail held out stiffly behind. The third eyelid becomes prolapsed, i.e. covers half the eye, and the horse becomes extremely nervous and sensitive to external stimuli. Saliva may drool from his mouth and the horse will eventually be unable to swallow. Severe sweating may occur and his temperature may rise to 43°C (110°F). The horse will finally go down and be unable to rise, the limbs extend, and convulsions and death often follow.

Treatment

This has to be aggressive and therapy is aimed at preventing further absorption of the toxin. The circulating toxin has to be neutralized with tetanus antitoxin although this will not stop the clinical signs as it is unable to penetrate nervous tissue already affected. High doses of penicillin are also given.

The horse should be kept in a dark, quiet stable and sedatives should be given to keep him tranquil. Once the horse is recumbent, however, the prognosis is very poor.

Vaccination

This is simple and highly effective. First aid and thorough cleaning of wounds will also help to prevent the disease.

Tetanus vaccine should be administered in two doses four to six weeks apart, followed by an injection one year later, and thereafter every 18–30 months.

Pregnant mares should receive a booster four weeks before foaling to ensure antibody protection for the new born foal. The foal should then be vaccinated at two, three and six months, and boosted after one year.

Orphan foals, and those born to unvaccinated mares, should be given tetanus antitoxin within two days of birth to provide immediate, although short acting, protection. Vaccination should then be administered as above.

To save time and money and also give maximum protection, a combination of vaccines for both equine influenza and tetanus can be given. Once the initial basic course of four injections has been given, the boosters for flu are required no more than every 12 months, whereas the tetanus boosters are required every 18–30 months. One of the following programmes should be adopted:

1. Basic course of four injections followed by:
   12 months later – first booster – equine influenza only
   12 months later – second booster – equine influenza and tetanus
   12 months later – third booster – equine influenza only
   12 months later – fourth booster – equine influenza and tetanus
   Then repeat

For horses competing regularly and therefore more at risk:

2. Basic course of four injections followed by:
   9 months later – first booster – equine influenza
   9 months later – second booster – equine influenza
   9 months later – third booster – equine influenza and tetanus
   Then repeat

Only vaccinate healthy horses, and if they are coughing inform your veterinarian. Occasionally horses can become quite ill following vaccination, and the majority of horses are definitely below par for a couple of days. Do not work the horse hard or expose it to stress by travelling for a week or so after the vaccination.

A list of other vaccinations which may or may not be required, depending on the location and use of the horse, is given below (ask your veterinary surgeon):

Equine herpes virus 1 (EHV-1) (also known as rhinopneumonitis or equine virus abortion). This virus may cause abortion in breeding stock and vaccination of pregnant mares is often valuable.

Viral encephalomyelitis (Eastern, Western and Venezuelan) This virus is communicable to man and causes paralysis. The disease is restricted mainly to North and South America. Vaccination is practised in areas where the disease is likely to occur.

Rabies A fatal viral infection. The disease is not present in the UK or Eire. This disease is notifiable. If the disease occurs the horse is destroyed on humane grounds. Vaccination is available but it is not widely used for horses.

Strangles This is a bacterial disease which affects the respiratory system. The bacterium responsible is *Streptococcus equi*, although respiratory viruses may also play a role. Vaccination is available (but not in the UK).

African horse sickness (dorvine) Occurs in Africa, Central and South America, Middle East and parts of Asia. This is a venereal disease transmitted at service. Horses will die if left untreated. There is an annual vaccination available for horses.

First aid and the injured horse

There is no doubt that the horse is prone to accidents and injuries, particularly when galloping around fields. Most of these are minor superficial wounds which require only a small amount of care and attention.

Occasionally wounds can be deep and nasty and require immediate attention. In these situations it certainly helps if the horse owner does not panic and institutes first aid procedures quickly and efficiently.

It is vital that every yard has a good first-aid kit. This should contain the following:

First-aid kit:

- Curved scissors
- Bandages – conforming ones which mould to the limb
- Adhesive bandages – e.g. Elastoplast which keeps dressings in place
- Antiseptic wash – e.g. Hibitane
- Dressings – should be non-stick, e.g. Melolin, Fucidin Tulle
- Poultice dressing – e.g. Animalintex
- Thermometer
- Sterile saline solution
- Antibacterial/anti-inflammatory ointment – Dermobion
- Roll of gamgee – (not cotton wool)
- Petroleum jelly
- Antibiotic powder/spray
- Clean bowl
- Clean towel

Note UK brand names are given here. They may vary from country to country.

Wounds to the skin

Skin and soft-tissue injuries are frequently seen in horses. There are two different types of healing depending on the wound itself:

1. First-intention healing – this is the preferred method of healing whereby the edges of the wound are held together (e.g. by stitching) and heal quickly. This occurs after surgical incisions or in clean wounds where there is no loss of skin. Infection of a wound will always result in the failure of first-

intention healing, therefore thorough cleaning is vital.

Wounds above the knee and hock heal well whereas those below do not, due to the poorer blood supply and excessive movement in these areas.

2. Second-intention healing – this is a much longer process and occurs when the edges of the wound have been torn apart and there is loss of tissue. Healing of the wound must wait until the gap between the torn skin edges has been filled with granulation tissue. The skin can then grow over. Excess granulation tissue often protrudes from the wound preventing the skin from healing over **(39)**. This is known as proud flesh (it stands proud of the skin surface) and has to be removed before full healing can take place. In some cases, skin grafts may be needed to aid healing of the skin.

There are various types of wounds and these can be broadly categorized into two groups: open and closed wounds.

Open wounds

Abrasions These are superficial skin wounds caused by rubbing or scraping. Examples are girth galls and saddle sores caused by ill-fitting tack and clothing.

Incised wounds These are clean with straight edges. They bleed freely and have very little bruising; they heal quickly by first intention. Examples are surgical incisions and cuts from glass.

Lacerations and tears These have torn edges and are usually irregular in shape. There is some bruising and variable bleeding. Often, tags or flaps of skin are present which have little or no blood supply, which leads to death of the flap. Such wounds are often caused by protruding nails, wire or posts (barbed wire in particular) **(40 and 41)**.

Puncture wounds These are potentially

39 Granulation tissue often forms on injuries below the knee/hock due to the relatively poor blood supply

serious and consist of small skin openings penetrating the soft tissue beneath. They are usually infected with bacteria and may contain foreign material. Punctures can result from bites, pieces of wire, or a horse staking itself on a jump or fence.

Penetrating wounds These are very serious as they enter deep into the body

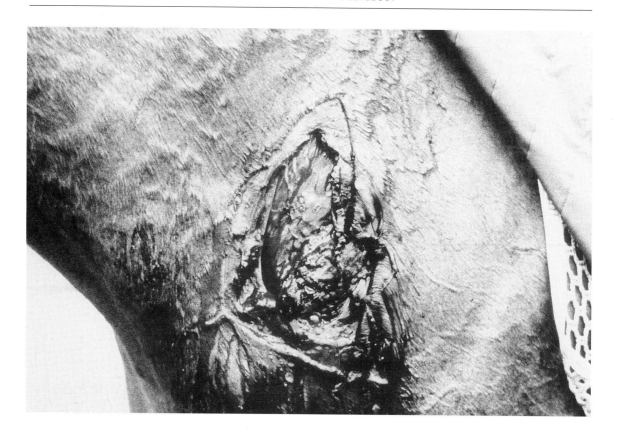

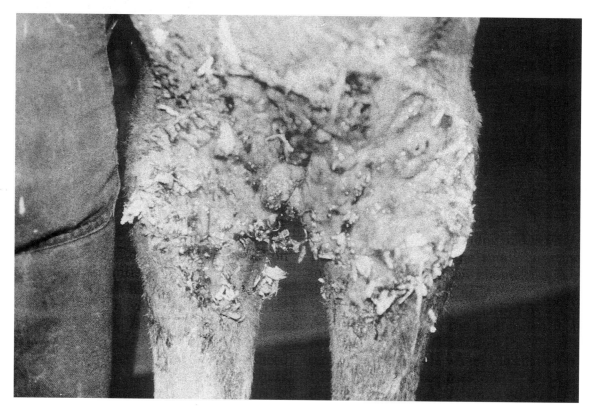

cavity, for example the chest or abdomen. Organs may be injured and emergency treatment is required from the veterinary surgeon. The wound should be covered to prevent damage or loss of internal organs, and to stop air being sucked into the body.

Closed wounds

Bruises These are very common, often resulting from kicks.

Contusions Caused by a blunt force inducing haemorrhage (bleeding), bruising and swelling without breaking the skin. Blood-filled swellings often form under the skin. This is known as a haematoma. Large haematomas will need draining after the bleeding has stopped. This should be done by the veterinary surgeon.

Sprains Damage to the ligaments which attach bone to bone around joints.

Tendon strains or ruptures Most common in the tendons of the forelegs as they are under greater strain. The tendon may partially or fully rupture and there is considerable swelling and pain on palpation. The horse may or may not be lame.

Muscle tears or ruptures This injury usually follows over-stretching of a fatigued muscle. There is variable lameness and inflammation. The horse should be rested.

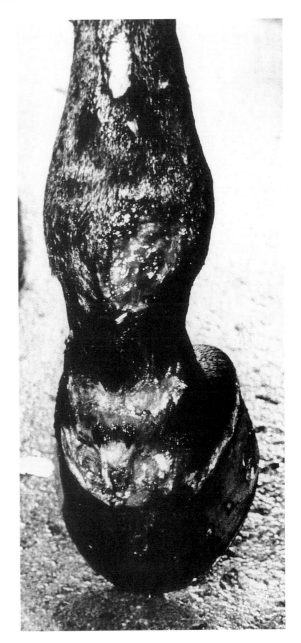

42 This injury involved penetration of the joint capsule. It is extremely serious and requires immediate veterinary attention

40 This laceration, although it looks nasty, healed rapidly after the subcutaneous layers were sewn back together

41 This injury is two weeks old. It was caused by a foal running into wire

The healing process

Whether the wound is a cut to the skin, a deep penetrating wound, tendon strain, ligament sprain or a broken bone, the healing process is the same and this begins with inflammation. This is a vital part of the repair process and results from the rupturing of cells, usually following trauma. **(Fig. 38)**.

Chemicals are released from the damaged cells causing the surrounding blood vessels to dilate. This creates heat at the site of the injury, the blood vessels become 'leaky' and white blood cells can then migrate to the injury site. This leaking from the capillaries causes swelling. The white blood cells break down the clot and surround any foreign material including bacteria. As this process continues the wound decreases in size which is known as wound contraction.

Inflammation can often be excessive and therefore needs to be controlled. Too much swelling will actually reduce the efficiency of the healing process.

Wound management and first aid

The immediate treatment of a wound or injury is extremely important as it can affect the long-term healing process. The following programme should be followed:

- Stop or control the bleeding by applying pressure to the wound.

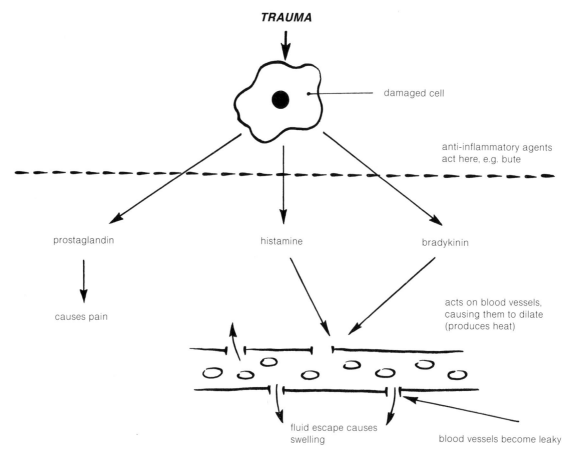

TRAUMA

damaged cell

anti-inflammatory agents act here, e.g. bute

prostaglandin

histamine

bradykinin

causes pain

acts on blood vessels, causing them to dilate (produces heat)

fluid escape causes swelling

blood vessels become leaky

Fig. 38 The inflammatory response to injury at a cellular level

- Call the veterinary surgeon a) if the horse is shocked or in severe pain, b) if the wound is dirty and/or may contain a foreign body, c) if the wound needs stitching, d) if tetanus vaccinations are not up to date.
- Protect the wound and prevent further damage.
- Clean the wound using sterile instruments if possible. Cut away the hair around the wound and bathe with cooled, boiled water or saline solution. If it is on the leg, cold hose it carefully making sure that dirt is not washed in. Finally, rinse the wound with a sterile saline solution using a syringe. With minor cuts and abrasions use dilute antiseptic to clean. Minor wounds are often best left uncovered to heal in the open air.
- Once clean, reassess the injury and if necessary call the veterinary surgeon. Otherwise, cover with a new dressing and bandage if possible **(Fig. 39)**. The dressing should consist of gauze squares soaked in petroleum jelly, or antiseptics/antibiotics which are available from the chemist. Next, pad with gamgee, followed by a conforming bandage. After three to four days (changing the dressing regularly), swap the impregnated gauze for a dry dressing.
- To help reduce the swelling which impedes healing walk the horse in hand, and bandage if possible **(43)**.

Many horse owners panic when they see a horse bleeding badly as they do not know how to control it. Tourniquets are not recommended. Control of bleeding depends upon the amount of haemorrhage and the extent of the injury.

Controling the bleeding:

Blood oozing Apply direct pressure with a clean piece of gauze. Do not dab or wipe the wound. Hold the wad in place for 10 second intervals and reapply until bleeding has stopped.

Blood flowing freely Apply heavy pressure with a wad of gauze. Wrap firmly (not too tight) with elastoplast/vet wrap for 30 minutes then re-evaluate the wound.

Arterial bleeding Characterized by bright-red spurting blood (spurts in time with the pulse). Apply very heavy pressure with a gauze wad. Wrap elastoplast/vet wrap tightly around the gauze as this helps to immobilize the edges of the wound. The veterinary surgeon must be called and until he/she arrives the horse should be kept quiet and still.

Bleeding from the nostrils Restrict horse's movement, keep quiet and calm. Apply ice packed in a towel to the nose.

Once the bleeding has stopped, the extent of the injury can be properly assessed and the wound can then be managed as above. Quite often, wounds will be dirty or become infected, and abcesses may develop. These need special care in the form of a poultice. Poultices are usually hot and are used to increase the blood supply to the area and draw fluid and infection from the wound, thereby cleansing it.

There are various types of poultice and one should be chosen to suit your particular need:

Animalintex This consists of a thick layer of padding containing bassorin and boric acid with polythene backing on one side to help retain the heat. It is a very useful poultice and all first-aid kits should contain a pack. This is currently only marketed in the UK.

Kaolin A grey paste which is stored in a tin. The tin is heated and the paste then applied to gamgee which is placed over the injury.

Bran with epsom salts This is most commonly used for foot injuries, particularly puncture wounds. Boiling water is

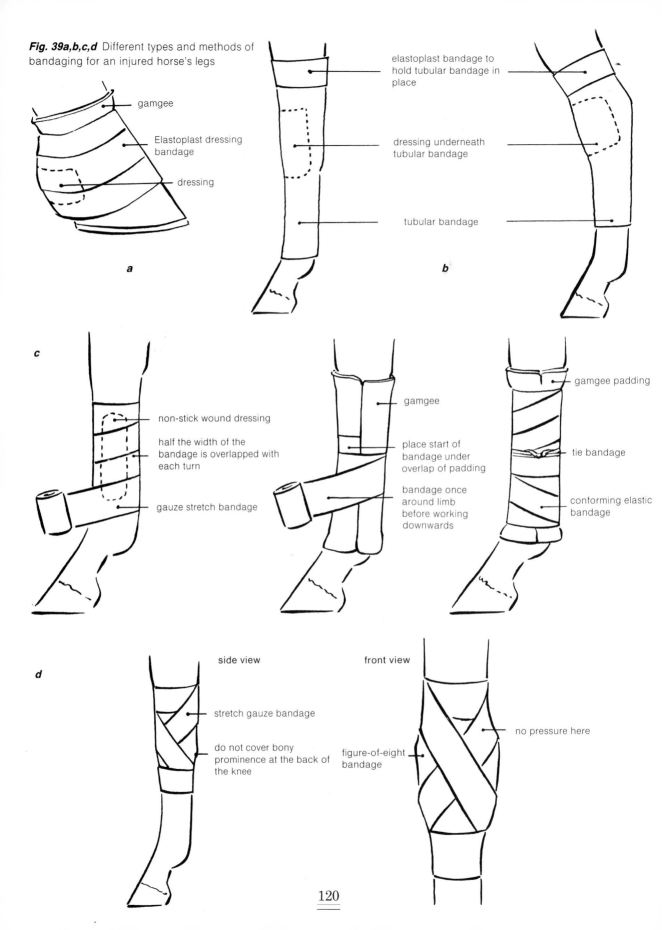

Fig. 39a,b,c,d Different types and methods of bandaging for an injured horse's legs

a

gamgee

Elastoplast dressing bandage

dressing

elastoplast bandage to hold tubular bandage in place

dressing underneath tubular bandage

tubular bandage

b

c

non-stick wound dressing

half the width of the bandage is overlapped with each turn

gauze stretch bandage

gamgee

place start of bandage under overlap of padding

bandage once around limb before working downwards

gamgee padding

tie bandage

conforming elastic bandage

d

side view

stretch gauze bandage

do not cover bony prominence at the back of the knee

front view

no pressure here

figure-of-eight bandage

120

43 To help reduce swelling the leg may be bandaged (not too tightly)

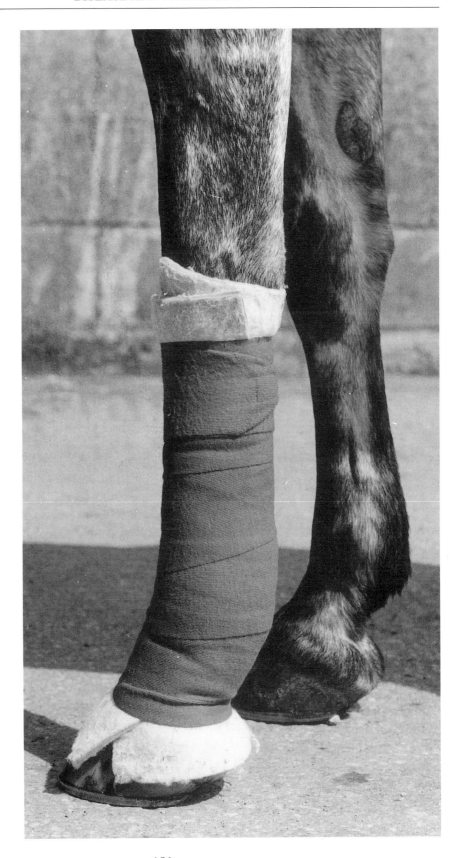

added to the mixture to make it damp and it is then applied to the foot, once it has cooled sufficiently.

Magnesium sulphate Again, this is a paste most often used for foot injuries. It should not be used on open wounds under any circumstances.

Injury sites can be in awkward positions where they cannot be effectively bandaged. If a poultice cannot be used another technique, known as hot fomentation, can be tried. A small clean towel is soaked in hot water in which Epsom salts have been dissolved. This is then applied to the area for 20 minutes and repeated two to three times per day. Two or three towels may be used at the same time: whilst one is being used on the horse the other can be soaked in hot water again. This is an effective method as it allows a high temperature to be maintained.

In the case of foot infections or abcesses the foot should be immersed in hand-hot water containing Epsom salts for approximately 10 minutes before the poultice is applied. This helps to draw the infection out. The foot should then be poulticed immediately.

Administration of medication

Horses often refuse medication (usually because of the taste) and this can be infuriating. Refusal can lead to a deterioration in condition and a waste of the medicine. There are various ways of administering drugs, the method usually depending upon the type of drug, the condition of the horse and its temperament.

Oral administration

This includes powders and liquids in feeds and water, and pelleted preparations.

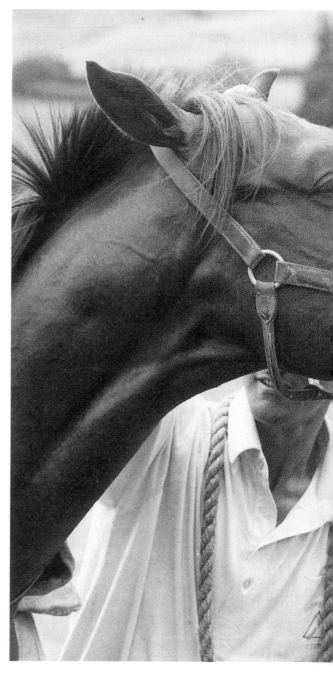

Often, preparations such as supplements (vitamins and minerals) are given in the feed and body salts (electrolytes) are given in the drinking water. If electrolytes are being added then some plain drinking water should also be made available for the horse.

Powders or pellets which the horse

refuses to eat can be masked with molasses, honey or peppermint essence.

Syringe

Pastes and liquids are often given by syringe, for example wormers and probiotics.

44 Tubing involves insertion of a tube up the horse's nostril and into the oesophagus. This may be done to administer medication, but should only be carried out by those qualified to do so

When using a syringe, make sure that the horse has a strong headcollar and you have assistance if you feel you need it.

Stand to the left-hand side of the horse's head and gently insert the syringe into the corner of the mouth, laying the nozzle on the surface of the tongue, and depress the plunger (make sure that you have removed the cap first). Afterwards, gently raise the horse's head until he has swallowed the paste. When giving a liquid by this method do not squirt it into the mouth but administer it very slowly to prevent the horse inhaling it into the lungs causing inhalation pneumonia.

Tablets, capsules and boluses

These are usually placed in the mouth. It is easiest to do this using a gag to keep the upper and lower jaws apart, enabling the horse owner to place the tablet or capsule as far back on the tongue as possible, without being bitten. If a gag is not available then the horse owner should stand to the left-hand side of the horse by the head and then gently but firmly grasp the tongue, pulling it out to the side of the mouth. The horse will not close his mouth as he would bite his tongue. The tablet can then be placed at the back of the mouth. The head should be gently raised to help the horse swallow.

The following methods of administration of drugs should only be undertaken by qualified people such as veterinary surgeons.

Drenching

This involves raising the horse's head high so that when a plastic bottle of liquid is placed in the corner of the mouth the liquid is slowly swallowed. Great care should be taken that fluid does not enter the windpipe, instead of the oesophagus, causing secondary pneumonia.

Stomach tube

This involves the insertion of a tube up the nostril into the oesophagus. Great care again is required to avoid the tube being inserted incorrectly into the windpipe causing death by inhalation pneumonia **(44)**.

Administration of drugs via the rectum

This must be undertaken very carefully, particularly in foals. A lubricated tube is gently inserted into the rectum to a distance of no more than 6 cm ($2\frac{1}{2}$ in). The fluid being administered can then be allowed to flow gradually by gravity into the rectum.

Administration of drugs by injection

This is one of the most commonly used methods by veterinary surgeons, due to its ease and efficiency. There are several methods of injecting the drugs, including intravenous (IV – into the vein), subcutaneous (under the skin), intra-muscular (into the muscle mass) and intra-articular (into the joint capsule). Which one of the above methods is used will be determined by the type of drug being administered.

8
COMMON PROBLEMS

8

COMMON PROBLEMS

Problems affecting the skin

When horses are turned out, particularly in bad weather, they become more prone to certain problems, mostly affecting the skin. A look at the basic structure of this organ is therefore appropriate.

The skin is the largest and most exposed organ. It is a complex structure which acts as a protective outer covering, preventing the entry of microorganisms, and is a major part of the body's immune or defence mechanism. The skin is also responsible for the synthesis of vitamin D in the presence of sunlight (UV Light), and it varies in thickness over different parts of the body. A simplified drawing of the skin structure is shown in **Fig. 40**.

The cells of the innermost layer of the skin reproduce themselves continuously and the older cells push up towards the epidermis (outermost layers) and are then worn away and flake off, as scurf. As the cells move to the surface they die and form a substance called keratin, a tough protein, which helps to waterproof and protect the skin. Keratin is also found in hooves and hair which are modifications of the skin.

Underlying the epidermis is the dermis which consists of loose connective tissue giving the skin its elasticity. Within the dermis are the sweat and sebaceous glands, hair follicles, blood capillaries and nerve endings. Each hair grows from a single follicle. The blood capillaries supply the skin with vital oxygen and nutrients and remove any waste products. These capillaries also help in temperature regulation, and in cold weather those near the surface constrict, reducing heat loss. In warm weather, or when the horse gets hot from exercise, the blood vessels dilate so that more heat can be lost through the surface.

The nerve endings in the skin are very sensitive, enabling the horse to respond to the rider's subtle instructions.

If the skin surface is broken then bacteria and other harmful agents can enter. Small cuts and abrasions should therefore be treated.

Ringworm

Ringworm is *not* a worm. It is a condition caused by one of two fungal species, namely *trichophyton* and *microsporum*. The lesions are quite characteristic but can vary. The first sign may be small patches of hair standing on end, usually in rings (hence ringworm). These hairs then fall out leaving circular patches of skin. Serum (a clear yellow substance) may seep

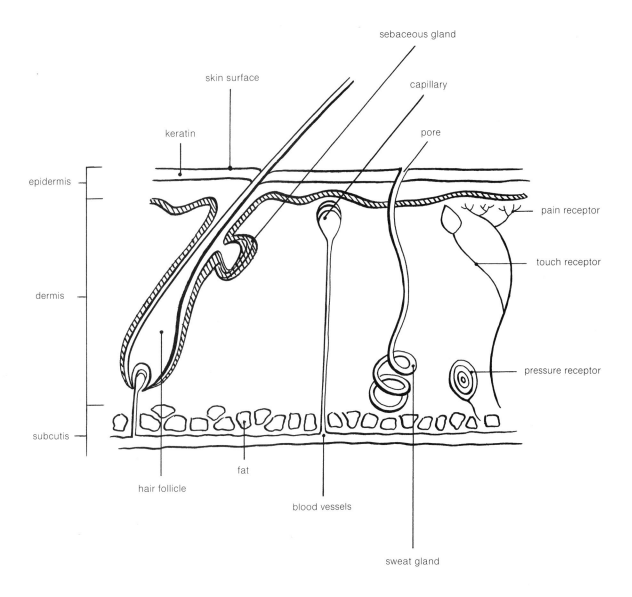

Fig. 40 Section through the horses' skin

from the patches which then crust over, and the skin will finally become scaly. The circular patches increase in size as the fungus spreads.

The most common sites on the body are in the girth and saddle areas, and the neck. It can be very unsightly. The incubation period is seven to 14 days.

The condition is self-limiting and can resolve itself over a period of two to three months if left untreated. However, it is extremely contagious and should be treated as soon as possible, before it spreads to other horses, or even humans. Unfortunately, the fungi produce millions of tiny spores which are released into the air. These can remain dormant in the ground for many years.

Treatment This consists of applications of anti-fungal ointments direct to the lesions, and usually does the trick if the condition is caught early on. However, if the ringworm has spread then drugs will also have to be administered systemically.

There are a wide variety of drugs available and you should consult your veterinary surgeon on the best one to use. Some can be harmful to pregnant mares.

Measures to prevent spread of infection

- Do not groom as this spreads the fungus into the coat.
- Do not clip, to avoid contaminating blades.
- Disinfect all grooming utensils, tack, rugs etc. with a fungicidal solution.
- Wash hands and boots thoroughly before dealing with another horse. Wear an overall.
- Do not ride the horse if there are lesions on the saddle or bridle area.
- Remember ringworm can be caught from cattle or cats.
- It can spread to humans so be very careful indeed.

Rain scald

This condition is commonly seen in horses which are permanently at grass, particularly in very wet conditions (45). It is caused by an actinomycete named *Dermatophilus congolensis* which enters via the softened wet skin. It is the same organism which is responsible for cracked heels and mud fever.

The most commonly affected areas are the dorsal line of the back and anywhere that water tends to collect, e.g. loins and shoulders. Removable tufts of hair are characteristically produced and attached to these are crusts of skin. Sometimes, if secondary bacterial infection is present there may be pus beneath the skin.

Rain scald is commonly seen in horses which are in poor condition or unthrifty. It is not contagious.

Treatment First bring the horse in and stable him, or leave him in a covered field shelter so that he won't get wet until the lesions have healed. Gently remove the tufts of hair and then treat the underlying skin with an anti-bacterial wash. If the infection is bad, consult your veterinarian as antibiotics may be required.

To prevent the condition recurring, turn the horse out in a New Zealand rug and check that the dietary requirements are being met.

Greasy heels, cracked heels and mud fever

These conditions, as previously mentioned, are caused by the organism *Dermatophilus congolensis*. They are very common and are characteristically seen in horses which are out in muddy or wet fields, particularly during the winter.

Right from the start tufts of hair can be seen (similar to rain scald), with crusts of skin attached. These are easily removed.

When the heels are affected (greasy heel), the skin deteriorates further and exudate is secreted into the heels making them 'greasy'. These can then develop into actual cracks in the skin (cracked heels) which may bleed and become very sore indeed. The horse may go lame and the lower limbs may swell.

Mud rash, or mud fever, is the same condition appearing on the lower limbs, particularly the hind legs.

Treatment This depends on the severity of the condition.

1. Mild cases – The horse should be stabled or kept in the field shelter on

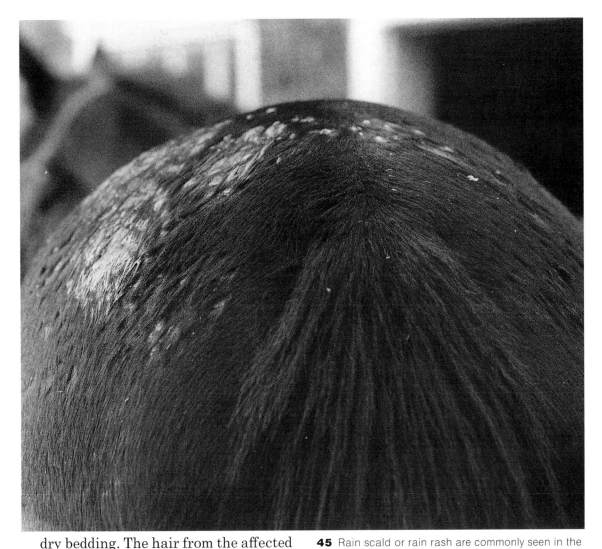

45 Rain scald or rain rash are commonly seen in the winter months

dry bedding. The hair from the affected area should be removed with curved scissors and the underlying skin washed with an anti-bacterial wash, and then thoroughly dried. Ointment is then applied. Dermobion is very effective (only currently available in the UK). The leg may then be covered with gamgee and bandaged for a couple of days to keep dry.

The horse should not be turned out until the skin has properly healed.

2. Severe cases – Again, keep the horse indoors. Remove the hair and then apply a poultice such as Animalintex to draw out the infection. Reapply twice over 24 hours, then allow the area to dry and apply an ointment such as Dermobion and bandage as above. If the condition is particularly severe, then a course of antibiotics may be required.

Prevention

- Do not brush the heels or legs when they are wet.
- Hose off muddy heels and dry thoroughly when the horse is brought in from the field.
- Clip the hair from the heels of suscept-

ible horses (particularly heavier breeds).

- Apply Vaseline or petroleum jelly to heels and pasterns before the horse is turned out to keep the areas dry.
- Some horse owners apply sunflower oil to the lower legs and heels before the horse is turned out to repel the water.

Sweet itch (summer seasonal recurrent dermatitis, Queensland itch, summer eczema)

Sweet itch is an allergic reaction to the bites of midges (*culicoides*). It is more common in ponies than horses although both can suffer. The reaction is to the saliva of the female midge, and as these are active from April to late October the problem is a seasonal one. Midges are most active at daybreak and nightfall and are most commonly seen near woods and water. They are extremely small which is why they have sometimes been called 'no see 'ums'.

The symptoms vary from occasional rubbing of the mane and tail to complete loss of the mane and upper tail hairs. The itching can be so severe that the horse develops open sores on the head, neck, withers and dock. Repeated rubbing over the years causes thickened scaly skin on these areas **(46)**. In some horses habitual scratching occurs and this continues into the winter months after the midge has ceased to be active.

Treatment In horses and ponies which are known to suffer, then prevention is better than cure. The following measures will all help:

- Stable affected animals from 4 p.m. to 8 a.m. in the summer months.
- Move affected animals away from ponds and woods if possible.
- Use a good long-acting fly repellant twice a day.
- Apply soothing lotions to the skin, such as benzyl benzoate.
- Where skin is very sore a corticosteroid cream may be required to help reduce inflammation and aid healing.
- For severely affected horses and ponies corticosteroid injections may be needed to reduce the inflammation and irritation. These can induce laminitis so great care should be taken. Discuss this with your veterinary surgeon.
- Adding garlic to the diet in the form of garlic oil can reputedly help the condition, although this has not been scientifically proven.

Sweet itch can be a real problem and affected animals need particular care and attention. Many susceptible ponies are sold in the winter months when the condition is not present, so prospective purchasers should check with the vendor first.

Affected animals should not be used for breeding as the condition is hereditary. If you suspect that the horse or pony has the condition steer clear.

46 Sweet itch can lead to self-mutilation in severe cases, as horses rub themselves (often violently) to try and relieve the irritation

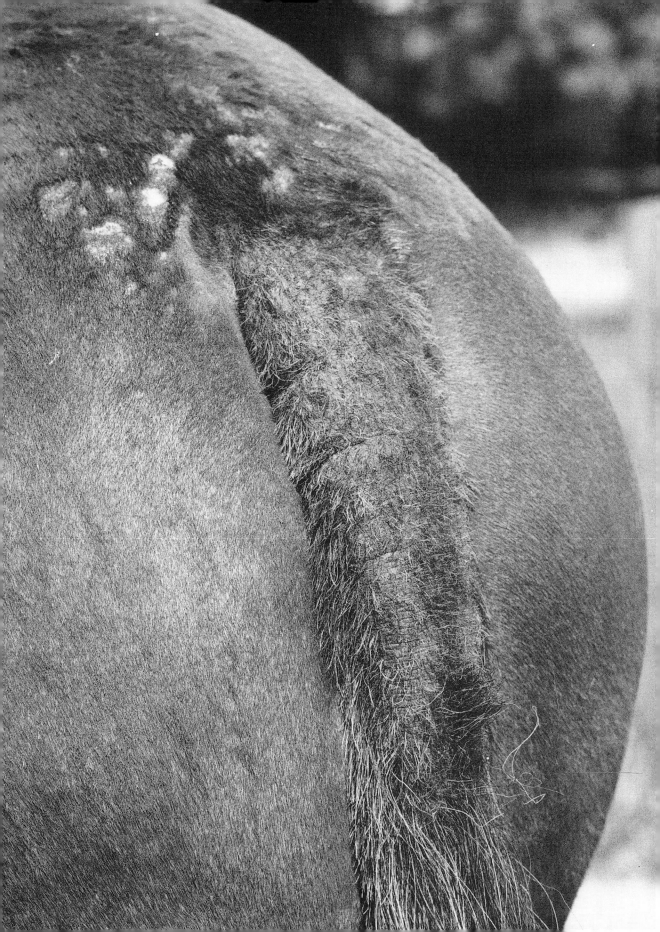

Urticaria (hives, nettle rash)

Another allergic reaction of the skin which may follow insect bites or ingestion of substances to which a hypersensitivity has been developed, such as food, drugs, nettles or other irritants.

The skin reacts to the allergen by releasing fluid into the skin and raised patches of variable size develop. They are not painful when touched, but they may be itchy. They tend to occur over the neck, chest wall and lower abdomen (47). Some allergic reactions may be particularly severe, with widespread swelling (oedema). This may extend to the respiratory tract and the horse may have difficulty breathing. The veterinary surgeon should be called immediately in this case.

A common allergic reaction can occur to high-protein diets, so these should be avoided, particularly in mature animals. Keep affected animals (but not youngstock) on a low-protein, high-fibre diet.

In severe cases antihistamines should be administered by the veterinary surgeon. It is important to try and find the cause of the allergic reaction so that it may be prevented in the future. Horses that have a known allergy, such as a respiratory one, are more susceptible to other allergies.

Reactions of the skin from contact with new bedding (e.g. a new bale of shavings) can result in widespread swelling under the belly, and on the neck if the horse has been lying down. The allergic response may be due to chemicals which have been applied to the wood from which the shavings were manufactured.

Photosensitization

A condition where pink skin reacts abnormally to sunlight (particularly the muzzle and nostrils).

Photosensitization occurs when the horse ingests certain agents from plants such as St John's wort and various clovers. These agents produce substances (during phases in their growth) which the horse ingests. These affect the skin in the presence of sunlight (the photosensitization response), causing damage. It can also be a side-effect of liver disease.

The affected skin soon becomes reddened and swollen and the skin may then peel off. The affected areas are very sore.

Treatment If liver disease is the underlying cause, then treatment and prognosis must be guarded. However, if it is due to a plant in the field then the horse should be brought indoors out of the sun for a week or so, until the lesions have healed. Clean the affected area carefully and gently as it will be very sore. Then apply an ointment such as Dermobion. The veterinary surgeon may be required to give an antihistamine injection.

Sunburn

This should not be confused with photosensitization. It is a normal reaction of unprotected skin to strong sunlight. The most commonly affected area is the muzzle, where the skin becomes sore and may peel.

Treatment Keep the horse indoors out of bright sunlight and apply an anti-bacterial soothing ointment. Prevent further burns by applying a strong sunscreen cream.

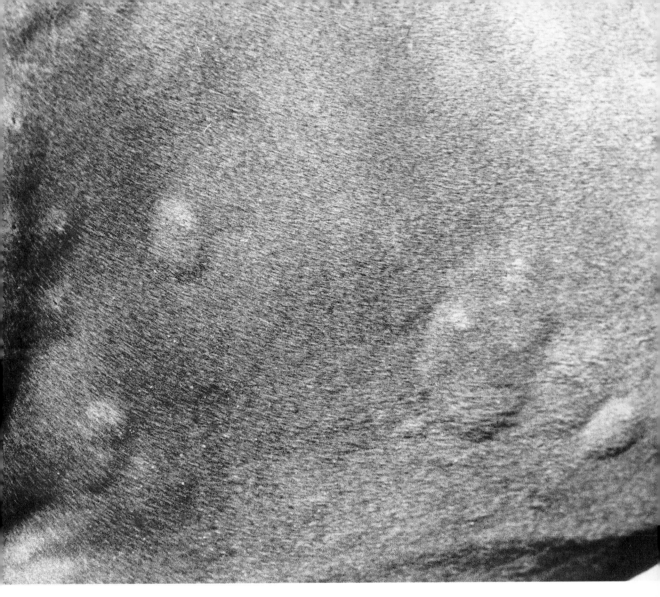

47 These raised patches of fluid-filled skin are known as urticaria, hives or more commonly nettle rash

Vitiligo

This is the name given to the loss of pigmentation, where the skin loses its dark colour becoming pink (48).

It can be caused by badly fitting tack or trauma to the skin. The resulting hair will grow back white. The condition can also arise spontaneously, particularly around the eyes and muzzle. This is a hereditary condition.

Treatment There is no treatment for this condition.

Lice infestation

There are two species of lice which affect horses, namely the sucking louse (*Haematopinus asini*) and the biting louse (*Damalina equi*) (**Fig. 41**).

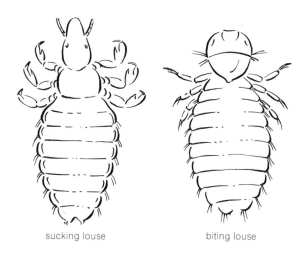

sucking louse   biting louse

Fig. 41 The two species of lice which affect horses

The sucking louse feeds on blood and the biting louse on scurf and debris on the skin-surface. They are both small, grey, slow moving and easily overlooked. They are just visible to the naked eye (1.5–3 mm long). The cream coloured eggs (nits) are attached to the hairs close to the roots. They spend their entire life cycle on the horse, which is complete within three weeks.

These lice do not live on humans; their specific host is the horse.

Lice cause itchiness as they move around and some horses, even with low numbers of lice, can become hypersensitive, showing extreme itchiness. The coat becomes dull and scurfy, particularly on the head and neck, and horses rapidly begin to look moth-eaten. They also begin to lose condition and this can be quite rapid. The lice and nits will be visible if closely observed with a hand lens.

Treatment Louse powder or anti-parasite washes should be applied liberally – obviously powders are preferred in cold weather. This should be repeated two and four weeks later to kill the lice which have hatched from the eggs. All other horses in the field should be treated at the same time as lice spread by direct contact.

48 Vitiligo is often seen around the eyes and on the muzzle of the horse. It is a loss of pigmentation of the skin

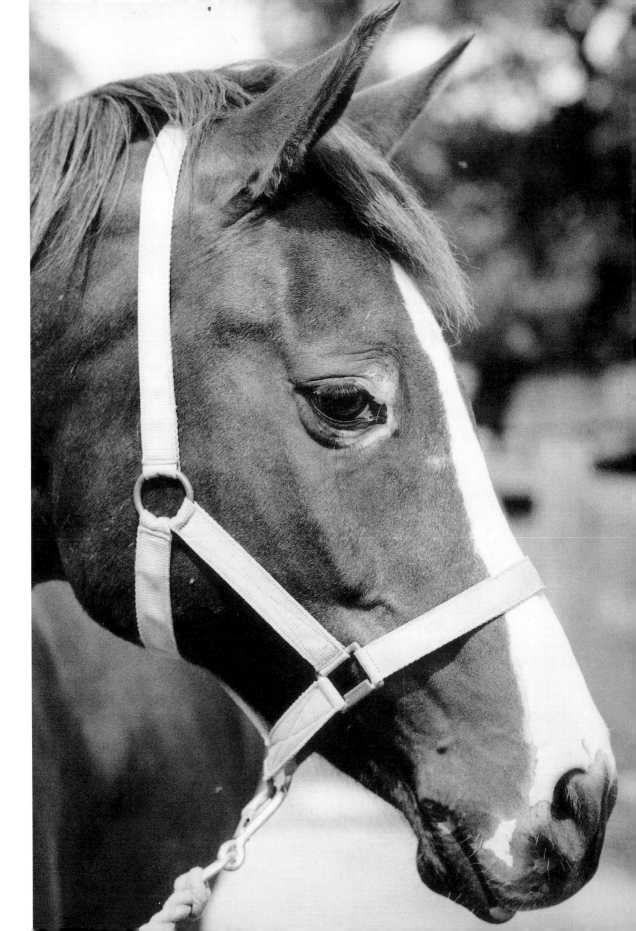

Common problems associated with the foot

The structure of the foot is shown in **Fig. 42**.

Pus in the foot (puncture wounds)

This is a major cause of lameness in horses. A foreign body, such as a nail or thorn, penetrating the sole or frog of the hoof will cause bruising and bleeding and

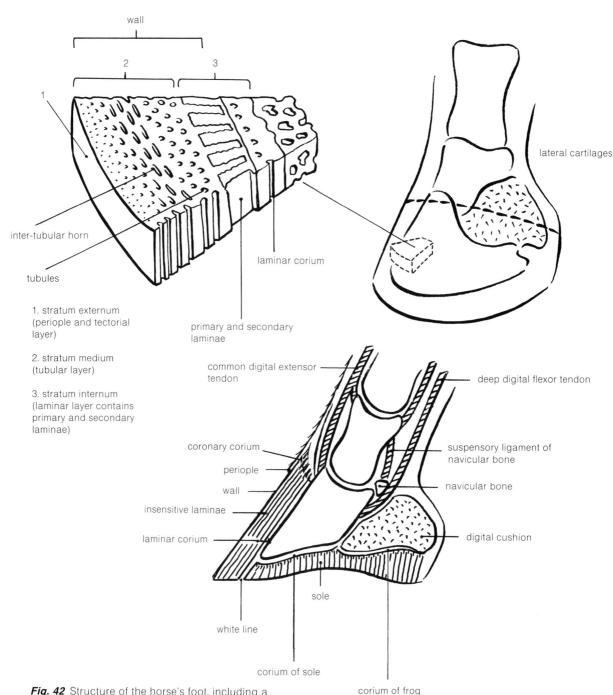

Fig. 42 Structure of the horse's foot, including a section through the hoof wall

wall

2   3

1

inter-tubular horn

tubules

1. stratum externum (periople and tectorial layer)

2. stratum medium (tubular layer)

3. stratum internum (laminar layer contains primary and secondary laminae)

laminar corium

primary and secondary laminae

lateral cartilages

common digital extensor tendon

deep digital flexor tendon

coronary corium

suspensory ligament of navicular bone

periople

navicular bone

wall

insensitive laminae

laminar corium

digital cushion

sole

white line

corium of sole

corium of frog

introduce bacteria into the hoof. Infection, a build-up of pus and an increase in pressure inside the hoof wall, will follow. This is very painful. If the condition is not treated at this stage the pressure will force pus along the line of least resistance which will eventually burst out from the coronary band. If not, it will burst out from the site of the initial injury if it is large enough. Only a minute prick is required to introduce infection.

Clinical signs The horse will often show a slight lameness in the early stages which quickly progresses to severe lameness where the horse is reluctant to place any weight at all on the affected foot. If the horse is in the field it may take some time to walk it back to the stable or shelter. This is usually accompanied by heat in the foot and a bounding digital pulse. Oozing of pus from the coronary band is a sure sign.

Treatment The veterinary surgeon should be called immediately. He will locate the site of penetration through 'pinching' the hoof with a pair of hoof testers until a particularly sensitive spot is found, and then drain the abcess by making a bigger hole at the site of injury for the pus to drain out of. This is a tremendous relief to the horse and they usually show a drastic improvement once this has been done. The shoe has to be removed first.

Next, in order to drain the infection completely, the foot is tubbed before being poulticed. Tubbing involves placing the foot in clean, salty, hand-hot water (49). The foot is left in the water (if the horse is cooperative) for 10 minutes and a poultice applied. An Animalintex poultice is normally used for foot injuries. Plastic boots can be used to keep the hoof clean (e.g. Equiboot). Tubbing and poulticing should be carried out twice a day for three to four days.

Sometimes the drainage hole is not big enough and a further visit from the veterinary surgeon may be required. Antibiotics will occasionally be prescribed if the infection is severe and the wound particularly deep.

When all evidence of infection and/or lameness associated with it has disappeared, then the hole may be plugged with some clean cotton wool, followed by Stockholm tar to seal it. A pad may be used under the shoe when it is replaced, to protect the healing sole. The horse should be given tetanus antitoxin if the vaccination programme is not up to date. This gives immediate but temporary protection.

Prognosis is generally good, but if a foreign body, such as a nail, has penetrated deeply and come into contact with such structures as the navicular bone and bursa, the coffin joint or the deep digital flexor tendon and its sheath then prognosis is guarded **(Fig. 43)**. The pedal bone

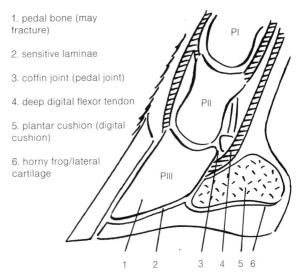

1. pedal bone (may fracture)

2. sensitive laminae

3. coffin joint (pedal joint)

4. deep digital flexor tendon

5. plantar cushion (digital cushion)

6. horny frog/lateral cartilage

Fig. 43 Possible sites of penetration of a puncture wound to the foot

may even have fractured. If a deep penetration is suspected, the veterinary surgeon must be called immediately. The horse's foot will be x-rayed using special radiographic techniques.

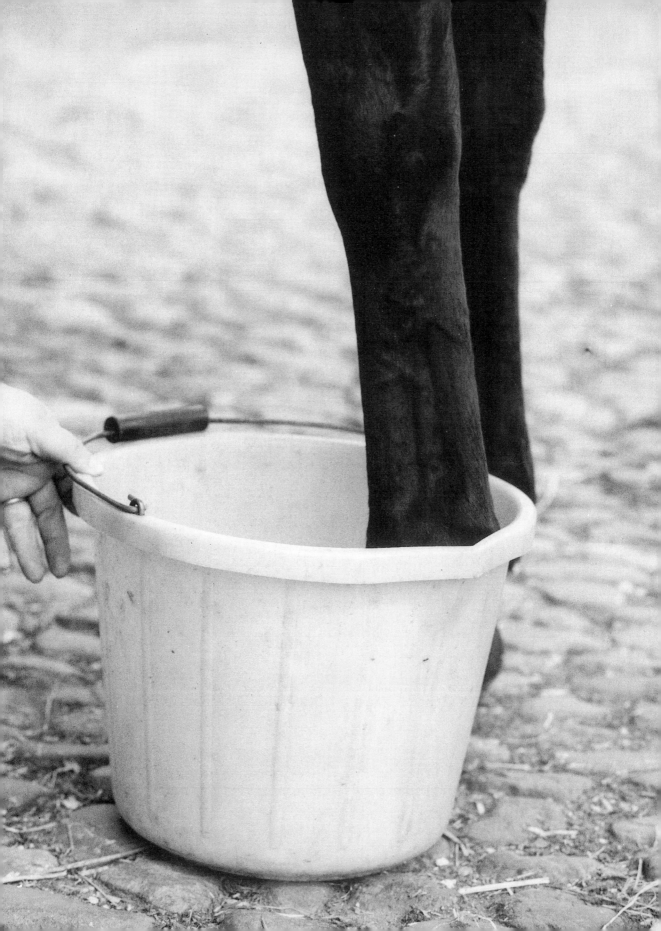

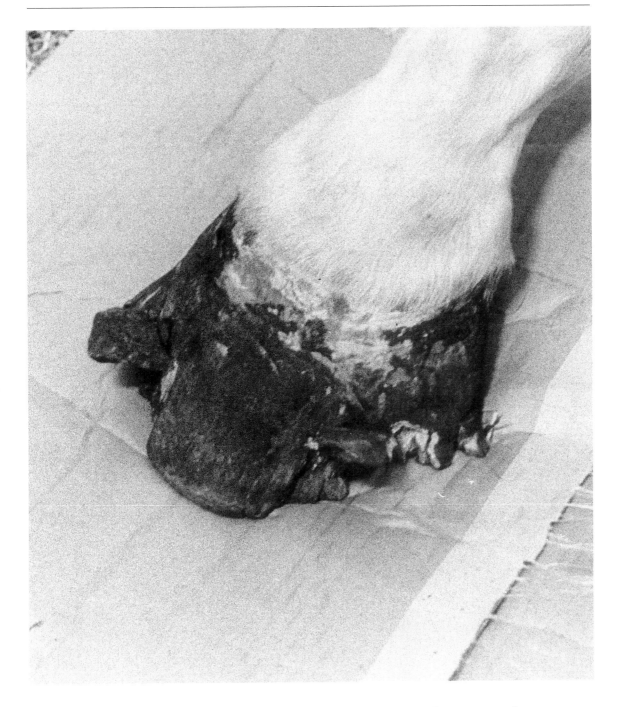

50 This pony has severe cracks originating from the ground surface

49 Tubbing the horse's foot – a routine which many horse owners will be familiar with

Sandcracks and grasscracks

These are cracks in the hoof wall. Sandcracks are those which begin at the coronary band **(50)**, and grasscracks begin at the ground surface. They are referred to according to their position on the hoof, such as toe, heel or quarter cracks.

Often these cracks are superficial with only the outer insensitive hoof wall affected. However, deeper cracks will affect the more sensitive inner tissues and the horse will most likely be lame **(Fig. 44)**. Heel and quarter cracks are more likely to cause lameness as the hoof wall is thinner in these areas.

These cracks may result from a number of causes including lack of proper care and trimming, poor hoof conformation (long toes and low heels), hooves affected by chronic laminitis, brittle hooves (see later) and thin hoof walls. Often, sandcracks result from injury to the coronary band such as an overreach.

The degree of lameness associated with the crack will depend on the extent to which the sensitive tissues of the foot are involved. In some cases the deeper cracks will result in infection with pus build up.

Treatment Will depend upon the degree of involvement of the sensitive parts of the hoof, if any. Superficial grasscracks can be prevented from carrying on up to the coronary band by carving deep grooves into the hoof wall at the top of the crack. This should be done by the farrier. Toe clips may also be used at the base of the crack.

Superficial sandcracks may be treated by attaching a toe or nail clip on either side of the crack until the hoof crack grows out. If the crack was caused by an injury to the coronary band, which is consequently permanently damaged, then the hoof wall will never grow down properly and the crack will be permanent. This is because the horn-producing cells in the coronary band are impaired.

If the cracks are infected then veterinary treatment will be required. The infec-

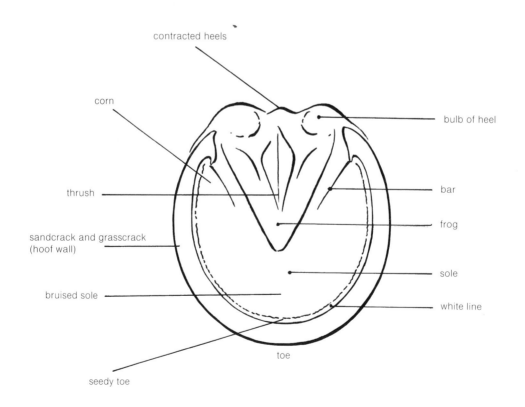

Fig. 44 Structure of the foot as seen from below, showing the sites of common problems

140

tion will have to be treated and drainage of the infected area established. The hoof wall will then be wired up and the crack filled with acrylic resin to prevent the entry of dirt.

Brittle feet

Some horses have slow-growing hooves with thin walls. These tend to develop multiple splits and cracks around the base of the hoof wall, particularly in the summer months. The hoof walls continue to crack despite regular trimming and shoeing and some horses are unable to keep shoes on. The cause of this condition has created much debate. The moisture content of the hoof wall is very important and this is controlled by a structure called the periople. Damage to this membrane may disturb the proper balance of moisture entering and leaving the hoof wall, leaving it more prone to cracking.

Treatment This is mainly aimed at encouraging healthy horn growth by the following techniques:

- Dietary improvement – Proper horn growth depends upon several vital nutrients including biotin, methionine, calcium and zinc. A supplement containing adequate amounts of all these micro-nutrients should be given. True biotin deficiencies are rare as the horse is able to synthesize this vitamin through the microorganisms in their own digestive tract. Supplements containing MSM (methyl sulphonyl-methane) may also be used. Any supplement has to be fed for at least a few months before any improvement can be seen.
- The feet should be regularly trimmed and shod.
- The feet should be treated with moisturizing creams which rehydrate the hoof wall. Hoof oils prevent the passage of moisture back into the hoof wall and so should be avoided.
- Daily washing of the feet with water and a sponge is beneficial. Do not scrub them as this will remove the periople.
- Daily application of Cornucrescine (only currently available in the UK) to the coronary band area may improve the growth rate of horn.
- Horses which have particularly brittle feet and cannot keep shoes on may benefit from the application of glue-on shoes. These are plastic and do not involve the use of nails. They will keep the horse in work but are more likely to come off when the horse is turned out.

9
SERIOUS PROBLEMS

Horses at pasture can be prone to really quite serious conditions such as grass sickness and laminitis. Luckily, the former is not common although the latter certainly is, particularly in the grass-kept pony. Colic is also common.

Grass sickness

Grass sickness is a serious threat to horses in Great Britain, particularly in some regions. Unfortunately it is quite difficult to diagnose in the living horse, and at present the ultimate diagnosis depends upon the removal of certain nervous tissue (autonomic ganglia) which shows characteristic changes with the onset of the disease. These can only be removed from the dead horse. Many of the symptoms of acute grass sickness are similar to severe colic and this can lead to diagnostic difficulties. The cause of grass sickness is still unknown.

Symptoms The disease occurs in four different forms, namely peracute, acute, subacute and chronic. These reflect the differing degrees in the manifestation of the same pathological changes in the nerves supplying the digestive tract. The changes lead to paralysis of the whole, or parts of, the gut from the pharynx to the rectum and digesta in the gut slows right down or stops, leading to impaction. Gut sounds are much reduced from normal, or may be non-existent, and any droppings which are passed are hard and black. Failure of the stomach to empty means that gastric contents and saliva accumulate and if the stomach becomes over-distended, the build up of pressure will lead to regurgitation of stomach contents through the nostrils. At worst, the stomach may rupture, with fatal consequences.

Other symptoms include sweating, muscular tremors and increased heart rate. The horse has difficulty swallowing and quickly becomes dehydrated. Horses with grass sickness usually show signs of severe abdominal pain (colic).

Acute cases die within a couple of days, subacute within three weeks, and chronic cases may go on for several months.

Treatment There is no known cure for the acute and subacute forms of this disease and in these cases prognosis is very poor. Euthanasia, to prevent any further suffering, should be carried out as soon as possible. Recent work at the Royal School of Veterinary Studies, Edinburgh, has shown that a recovery rate of 64 per cent is now possible in horses suffering from the chronic form.

The disease has a high incidence in certain geographical areas and particular fields can be linked with grass sickness. In a recent survey, 75 per cent of victims had undergone a major change in management shortly before the illness.

Grass sickness has been statistically shown to be associated with:

- Two- to seven-year-old horses.
- Horses kept solely out at pasture.
- March–June.
- Horses which have recently arrived on the premises.
- Pastures where the disease has previously occurred.

Grass sickness is not a contagious disease.

If you suspect or know that a horse has had grass sickness when grazed on certain pasture or fields then do not turn them out onto it. It has also been suggested that newly arrived horses should be part stabled until they have settled in to their new environment.

Laminitis (founder)

This is one of the most severe and misunderstood diseases. Unfortunately, it is very common in grass-kept horses and ponies. It is particularly common in the spring and summer months and if it is pasture-caused it can occur in autumn when there is a late flush in the grass growth. This can catch horse owners unawares.

Laminitis is in fact the end result of a chain of events which can be started by a number of trigger factors. It can affect any horse at any time of year, although previously affected horses and ponies are more susceptible to further attacks.

The term laminitis means inflammation of the sensitive laminae of the horse's foot. These laminae are situated between the pedal bone and the hoof wall and attach the hoof to the bone by an interlocking mechanism between the sensitive laminae (on the pedal bone) and the insensitive laminae (on the inside of the hoof wall).

They also contain blood vessels which nourish the hoof, providing it with essential nutrients. The various trigger factors cause the blood pressure to rise which in turn leads to an increased blood supply to the feet. The blood supply shunts through the coronary band area and bypasses the hoof, resulting in reduced or cessation of the blood to the sensitive laminae. Once the blood supply is affected in this way, the cells of the laminae die. Inflammation then causes swelling, the release of certain chemicals including prostaglandins, and severe pain. Unless the cause is removed and the horse treated to prevent further damage, then the pull of the deep, digital, flexor tendon mechanically causes the separation of the dead, sensitive laminae from the insensitive ones and the rotation of the pedal bone. The sole may then drop **(Fig. 45)**. In severe cases the pedal bone may protrude through the sole and in acute cases this can occur very quickly.

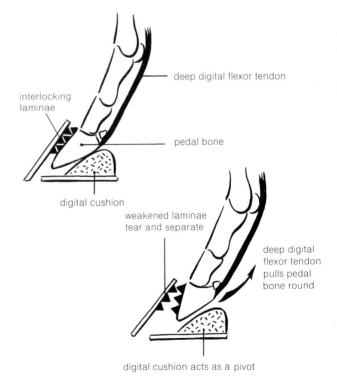

Fig. 45 The forces at play when separation of the laminae occurs in laminitis

Acute laminitis This is characterized by extreme pain in the feet, a bounding digital pulse and heat in the affected hooves. When standing, the horse attempts to keep as much weight as possible off the toes and rests on his heels producing the characteristic laminitic stance **(51)**. The horse's temperature may increase to 41.1°C (106°F) and the respiratory rate may rise to 50–70 breaths per minute. If the feet are examined (the horse may be in too much pain) the sole may have dropped and the pedal bone rotated. X-rays are required to determine the amount of rotation.

Chronic laminitis After the initial inflammation has subsided (which may take several days) the horse may develop chronic laminitis. This is characterized by intermittent or persistent lameness and a diverging growth pattern around the hoof wall (laminitic rings). These rings result from rotation of the pedal bone which compresses the blood supply to the coronary band. This slows down the rate of growth of new horn at the toe leading to rings which are wider at the heel than the toe. The hoof may have a high heel and be long in the toe, and the sole may have

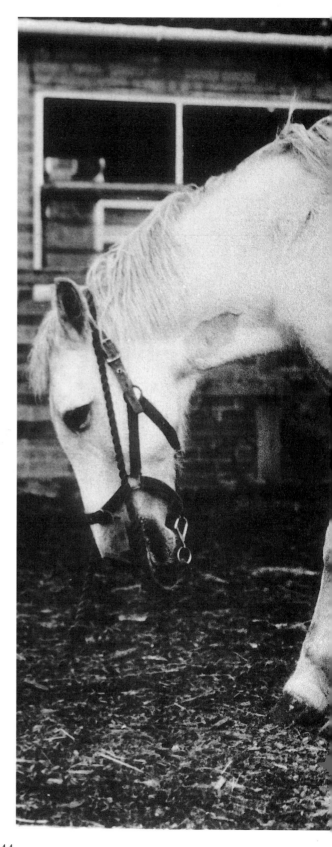

51 This pony has acute laminitis and is showing the characteristic laminitic stance. This is an emergency: veterinary treatment is required immediately to prevent further damage

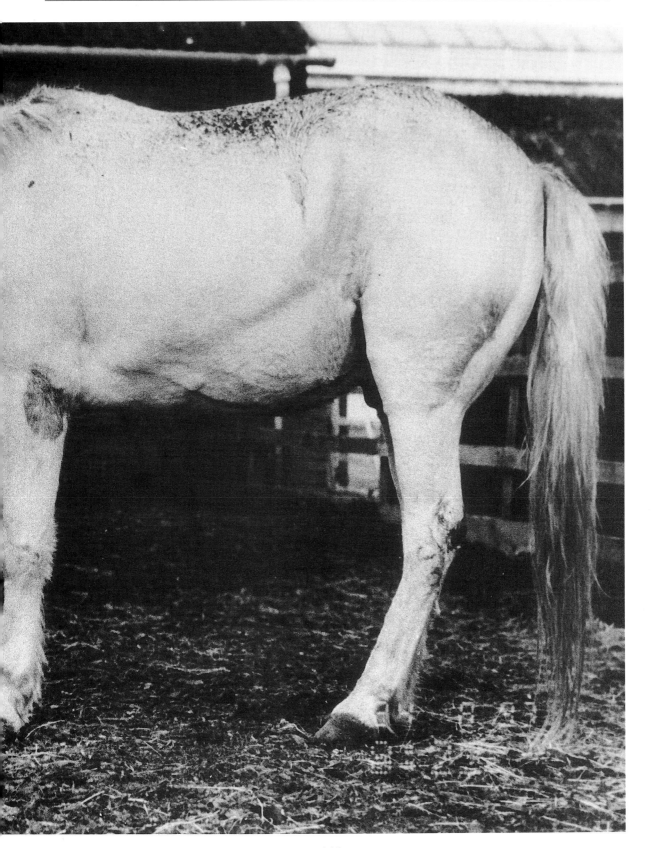

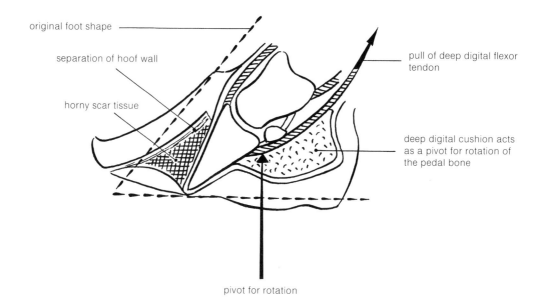

original foot shape

separation of hoof wall

horny scar tissue

pull of deep digital flexor tendon

deep digital cushion acts as a pivot for rotation of the pedal bone

pivot for rotation

Fig. 46 A chronic laminitic foot showing rotation of the pedal bone

dropped **(Fig. 46)**. A horse or pony suffering from chronic laminitis may be prone to acute attacks.

Treatment Laminitis is always regarded as an emergency as prompt veterinary treatment can result in a much better prognosis. The first aim is to relieve pain, followed by restoration of the blood supply to the feet. In the long term, the pedal bone has to be stabilized which can take many months. This often begins with surgical dorsal wall resection, followed by corrective trimming and shoeing under veterinary supervision.

The horse owner can help by first of all providing the horse with a deep bed of shavings or peat as this will pack the hoof and give vital support. He should have the concentrate part of the ration removed and be given hay. A vitamin/mineral supplement containing biotin, calcium, methionine and zinc can be mixed with a small

Common trigger factors

- Grain excess: over-eating grain or concentrates, particularly in ponies or horses which have managed to find their way into the feed room. If this happens the veterinary surgeon should be called as a matter of urgency. Do not wait for the symptoms to develop.
- Pasture founder – this follows grazing of pasture which has probably undergone a recent flush of growth. Some susceptible horse and ponies need to be watched carefully throughout the summer and have their access to grazing limited.
- Road founder – following excessive road work and severe concussion to the foot/feet.
- Drug-induced laminitis – horses receiving corticosteroid treatment may become laminitic.
- Toxaemia – e.g. retained placenta after foaling, severe diarrhoea or colic, where the bacterial toxins are absorbed into the blood system.
- Pituitary gland tumours may cause laminitis. This is particularly common in older horses and ponies.

amount of a high fibre feed such as Dengie Hi-Fi (a mixture of chopped hay, straw and alfalfa). The horse should not be starved or further problems may result.

Do not attempt to move the horse or walk him if the pedal bone has rotated as further damage may result.

There are many old wives' tales concerning the immediate treatment of laminitis. One in particular recommends that laminitic horses should be stood in cold, running water, such as a brook or stream. This may give some temporary relief from pain, but it also results in constriction of the blood vessels thereby exacerbating the problem.

Prevention Once a horse has had an attack of laminitis the horse owner should be extremely careful about his future management. Grazing should be carefully watched and if necessary restricted, particularly at times of rapid grass growth – a long dry period followed by rain will result in a flush. Overweight animals with a cresty neck should always be watched.

Do not overfeed with concentrates and keep susceptible horses and ponies on a high-fibre ration using high-fibre, low-energy feeds, e.g. a low-energy, chaff-based mix (Meadowsweet in the UK), or chopped hay, straw and alfalfa mix (Hi-Fi in the UK). Native ponies do not suit high concentrate rations at all.

Try to be aware of the common trigger factors and take immediate action if they happen to your horse or pony.

Colic

There are many different types of colic, with as many causes. The word colic means simply abdominal pain, and indeed the problem may be found in any part of the gut. It is extremely common and in its most severe form it is one of the major causes of premature death. It occurs in different degrees but is always a cause for concern, and veterinary advice should be sought. A large majority of cases will recover of their own accord within one to two hours, but the remaining cases require immediate action. Do not wait to see if your horse is in this group.

The pain usually results from stretching or inflammation of the gut lining (the lining is known as the peritoneum). Most colics are characterized by the following signs:

- Restlessness
- Pawing the ground
- Tail twitching
- Getting up and down frequently
- Loss of appetite
- Looking at the flanks
- Snorting
- Rolling and thrashing around (in severe cases) **(51)**
- Attempting to urinate frequently
- Lack of intestinal sounds (not in all cases)
- Sweating – usually patchy, increases with the severity of the condition
- Dehydration
- Constipation
- Increased respiration rate: from 12–20 to as high as 70 breaths per minute
- Increased heart rate: from 40 to as high as 90 beats per minute
- Increased body temperature

Spasmodic colic This is the most common type of colic and is caused by spasm of the muscular wall of the intestine. There are many possible reasons for this: damage to the intestinal wall by migrating worm larvae – particularly large strongyles (redworm), feeding too soon after exercise, and sudden change of diet.

Affected horses show moderate signs of distress. They pass only a few droppings and keep standing up and lying down. The condition seems to come and go, spasms lasting for a couple of minutes to half an hour. Recovery usually occurs without

treatment but pain relief and the use of spasmolytic drugs (relaxants) will help.

52 Horses with colic often roll violently. They will roll and get up continually

Impactive colic This is the second most common type of colic and is caused by impaction of food in the large intestine. The blockages tend to occur where there is a marked change in diameter and/or direction of the gut, and these occur typically at the pelvic flexure. Sometimes the small intestine may become impacted as a result of excess concentrates, perhaps after a binge in the feed room. It can also occur when a horse has eaten a large amount of straw bedding. Affected horses show less signs of pain than those with spasmodic colic. They lie down and look off colour, go off their feed and they may roll and look at their flanks. The site of impaction can normally be determined by the veterinarian through rectal palpation.

Treatment consists of dosing large volumes of liquid paraffin given by sto-mach tube for impactions higher up the gut, and an enema of warm soapy water for blockages of the large bowel. The aim is to lubricate the blockage so that it can be passed. Painkillers also need to be given.

Gas or flatulent colic This is often secondary to an impaction colic as gas is trapped in the gut. The pain is caused by gaseous distension of the gut wall known as tympany. It is usually extremely painful and affected horses show severe colic symptoms including violent rolling. The intestine may be twisted which results in the gas build up and pain. Excessive fermentation of feed in the intestine can also cause the symptoms. Gas colic frequently occurs in horses fed a rich concentrate diet, for instance brewers' grains in large amounts. Another common cause is the feeding of grass clippings which rapidly undergo fermentation in the gut producing large amounts of gas. Grass cuttings should not be fed to horses under any circumstances.

Veterinary attention is urgent. If there is a risk of the horse injuring itself then he should be quietly walked or left alone. The gas has to be released, usually by the insertion of a tube into the gut to allow it to escape. Often the horse needs to be anaesthetized and an exploratory operation performed to find the site of the distension.

Sand colic In sandy soil areas horses often ingest large quantities of sand, which can be seen in the droppings. Sometimes the sand forms large stones called enteroliths that will often need surgical removal. Sand colic frequently recurs as the horse continues to take in more sand. Signs include anorexia, diarrhoea, pawing the ground and looking towards the abdomen. Treatment of this kind of colic needs large doses of liquid paraffin to remove the sand.

Twisted gut (intestinal catastrophe) This is the most painful and dramatic type of colic. The intestine actually becomes twisted and/or parts of the bowel telescope into sections. This is known as intussusception. The twisting causes problems with the blood supply to the gut, and the affected horse shows extreme signs of pain, excessive sweating, violent rolling and overall distressed behaviour. There is a rapid rise in respiratory and heart rates. The veterinary surgeon should be called immediately as the horse will collapse, and even die, if major abdominal surgery is not performed. Quick referral for surgery will improve the prognosis. However,

---

Factors which may induce colic

- Exercising horses too soon after feeding. Leave for at least an hour before working him.
- Sudden access to concentrates or very lush clover-ridden grass.
- Stress, e.g. movement of horses to studs or different stables.
- Exhaustion.
- Drinking cold water whilst still hot after work.
- Feeding mouldy feed or forage.
- Poor worming programmes.
- Lack of regular attention to the teeth.
- Feeding too many concentrates and too little forage. The balance of forage to concentrates in the diet must be maintained.
- Feeding should be little and often, i.e. not one large concentrate feed per day.

---

in many cases humane destruction is the only option.

Chronic obstructive pulmonary disease (COPD)

Other names for this condition include: broken wind, heaves, equine asthma and alveolar emphysema.

Chronic obstructive pulmonary disease (COPD) is an allergic condition of the respiratory tract. It is a well known fact that horses with this disease benefit greatly from time spent outdoors, out of the stable environment. Stabling horses with COPD in poorly ventilated stables, on the wrong type of bedding, with poor quality hay, can exacerbate the problem to such an extent that the horse is no longer capable of any form of work.

Occasionally in the summer months horses may develop a similar condition known as pasture associated pulmonary disease (PAPD) in response to pollen from trees or grass. Oilseed rape, which is currently a popular agricultural crop producing the characteristic yellow fields, is suspected as being a common cause of this condition. Sometimes the horse may need to be moved to another yard, away from the offending pollen, until the pollen count has decreased.

Cause This is a chronic condition which results from horses becoming hypersensitive to organic antigens in the stable environment, such as fungal spores and dust. The antigens cause an asthma type reaction. The spores of some fungal species such as *Aspergillus fumigatus* and the actinomycete *Faenia rectivirgula* (formerly known as *Micropolyspora faeni* which causes the human condition farmers lung) appear to be the most important agents in Britain. Elsewhere,

however, other antigens are responsible and horses may be sensitive to more than one causative agent.

The antigens are small enough to be inhaled into the bronchioles of the lungs **(Fig. 47)** where they cause an inflammatory response resulting in spasm of the smooth muscle of the lower airways and increased production of mucus. Both these effects result in reduced space in the airways.

Clinical signs Horses can contract COPD from the age of two onwards; the older they get the more commonly the disease occurs. The condition develops over a period of time and as it progresses the horse's symptoms become gradually

Fig. 47 The airways of the horse's head

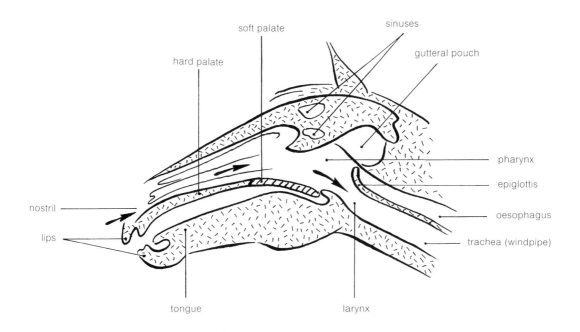

worse. The symptoms vary according to the severity of the disease.

Early signs include an occasional cough, usually at the onset of exercise, slightly increased respiratory rate and expiratory (breathing out) effort, and a white nasal discharge after exercise and first thing in the morning. Horses may demonstrate a reduced capacity for work and tire easily.

As the condition progresses, the affected horse will cough more frequently, particularly during exercise, but also at rest in the stable. A thick yellow nasal discharge may develop and horses may cough up lumps of yellow mucus. The respiratory rate can increase to 20 breaths per minute or more, and breathing out requires considerable assistance from the abdominal muscles to force air out of the lungs. This effort is double phased, with the result that horses often develop the characteristic heave lines along the abdomen. Very severe cases can result in wheezing, similar to asthma attacks in humans, and horses may develop acute respiratory problems. Horses do not have a temperature with this disease and they can look quite well although, more often than not, as the condition progresses the horse's coat becomes dull and lifeless and he can lose weight. Appetite is not usually affected.

Exposure to the causative antigen in affected horses results in changes to the small airways of the lungs. These include inflammation, spasm of the muscles of the bronchiole walls and the production of mucus. The airways (as we have seen) become narrower and there is less room for air to be breathed in and out. As the horse exhales the pressure reduces the diameter of these airways even further and some collapse completely. This in turn makes the removal of air from the lungs even more difficult and an increased amount of air is retained in the alveoli **(Fig. 48)**. This causes a 'ballooning' effect in the alveoli and an over-inflated appearance (the alveoli return to normal size

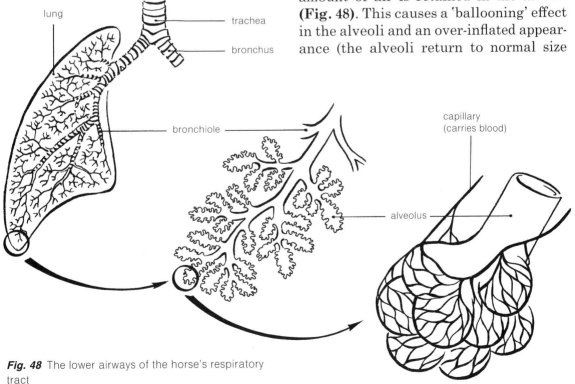

Fig. 48 The lower airways of the horse's respiratory tract

with remission of clinical symptoms). All these changes result in reduced oxygen supply to the affected horse.

Once the antigen is removed (by changing management practices) the symptoms will gradually disappear and the horse may remain free of clinical signs for long periods of time. However, he does not lose his hypersensitivity, so further exposure to the causative agent will re-establish the condition.

Diagnosis As soon as clinical signs are noticed the veterinary surgeon should be called. Early treatment can prevent long-term problems with this disease. The veterinary surgeon may listen to the horse's lungs with a stethoscope to detect changes in lung sounds, and in some cases an endoscope will reveal thick characteristic muscus in the trachea (upper wind pipe). In the early stages, however, changes in lung sounds may not be noticeable.

Treatment and prevention All COPD-affected horses need to be given a minimal dust environment. This aims to remove the causative agents from the vicinity of the horse and therefore allow the lungs to heal and return to as near normal condition as possible. Sometimes drug treatment will also be required but they should not be used on their own without making the appropriate changes in the horse's management.

The preferred and most beneficial method is to keep the horse at grass (provided they do not suffer from PAPD). The pasture should be away from hay and straw storage areas and dry hay should not be fed (unless it has been vacuum extracted to remove the dust and spores). Barn-dried hay will not have been affected by weather during the drying process and will therefore contain less fungal and mould spores. It will, however, need proper storing to prevent it becoming

dusty. Traditionally-made hay may need to be soaked to swell the spores to a larger size so that they no longer cause an allergic response. Alternatives to hay (and straw) may be used. Vacuum-packed forage has been developed and this is dust free. It consists of grass which has been cut and wilted to about 50 per cent moisture, and then compressed and baled. Feed should be in the form of cubes or molasses mixes which keep the dust levels down.

Straw should not be used as bedding in field shelters. Use wood shavings but do not allow it to become deep litter as the production of offending moulds will be higher.

Horses which are mildly affected should be lightly worked to help mobilize and remove the mucus from the respiratory tract. If they have moderate to severe breathing problems do not exercise.

Drug treatment Pharmaceutical agents used in the relief of COPD are as follows:
- Bronchodilators – e.g. Ventipulmin (clenbuterol hydrochloride). These drugs relieve the spasm of the muscles in the walls of the bronchioles.
- Mucolytics – e.g. Sputulosin (denbrexine). These drugs reduce the viscosity of the mucus in the airways making it easier for the horse to remove it by coughing.
- Prophylactic treatment – e.g. Cromovet (sodium cromoglycate). Helps prevent further attacks once the horse's clinical signs have been reduced. It consists of fine droplets of spray which are inhaled through a special mask and nebuliser. (The nebuliser is responsible for forming a spray of liquid particles which are breathed in).

Bronchodilators and mucolytics are most often given in the feed but in more severe cases injections may be required.
Note Brand names may vary from country to country.

APPENDIX

APPENDIX

Security and insurance

Horse theft and related crimes are increasing. There is nothing so distressing as arriving at the horse's paddock to find him gone. Thieves are not particular in the type of horse that they will steal. Well-managed horses are more easily loaded into transport and removed from the area, but there are certain security measures which the horse owner can undertake to reduce the risks.

First, make sure that horses in your care cannot be easily seen from the road, particularly if it is a busy one. Screen fencing can be erected or fast-growing, tall hedges planted. In an ideal situation the horses should be able to be observed from the house or stables, but if this is not possible then they should be visited twice daily especially if they are out permanently. Try varying your times so that no one is aware of a routine. It makes sense to avoid turning horses out with their head-collars on as this makes them easier to catch. However, problems may then be encountered by the owners themselves! Horse owners should be wary of strangers and politely challenge anyone they are unsure of.

Fencing and gates need to be secured (to keep thieves out and horses in). All gates should be locked (**53**) and the fencing checked regularly. Particular care should be taken with gates as they can easily be lifted off their hinges whilst the other end of the gate is chained and padlocked. Old railway sleepers (ties) or telegraph poles can be used as gate posts and are most secure when fixed in concrete. Gates should not be placed on public roads and if possible restricted to private roads or drives, preferably where they can be seen from the house/tack room. Tack rooms should be secured with padlocks if an insurance claim is to be taken seriously.

53 All gates should be securely locked

Thick hedges are ideal because they are generally difficult to cut through. A double barrier with barbed wire on the outside and then safer fencing on the inside is a good idea as long as the horses cannot reach the barbed wire. Ditches may be made deeper and wider to discourage thieves.

Horses may be given a permanent mark such as a freeze mark which is applied to the skin. There are also semi-permanent methods of marking horses, such as hoof marking, where a number is etched into the top of the hoof wall just below the coronary band. This is easily visible even when the horse is rugged up. It will last until the hoof grows out when it will need to be renewed. This can therefore be expensive.

Freeze marking

This is a method of branding which although not actually painful may be uncomfortable when applied. Chilled markers are usually placed under the saddle area or on the shoulder. The pigment cells responsible for hair colour are destroyed and the hair grows back white, in the shape of the markers used – usually an identification number which is then placed on a national register **(54)**. There is an initial fee for the operation and registration. Horses should be rested for up to three weeks afterwards, until the freeze mark has formed.

It is well known that this is the most effective deterrent and horse thieves will usually avoid freeze-marked horses although they may not know the horse is marked until too late. Freeze mark companies will be alerted as soon as the horse is stolen, and they will work with the police and slaughterhouses, ports and horse sales until the horse is found. Many insurance companies now offer reduced premiums for freeze-marked horses.

Insurance

Horse insurance is an extremely competitive business and companies spend a great deal of money marketing their policies in the equestrian press. It can become very expensive, particularly when an owner has several horses. There are various options for cover which include permanent loss of use, veterinary bills and public liability. Although it is not a legal requirement that horses be insured it is wise to at least have third-party liability insurance which protects the owner against claims and legal costs arising from damage caused by a horse or horses. Some British equestrian societies automatically provide this cover with membership, such as the BHS (British Horse Society), BSJA (British Show Jumping Association) and the Pony Club. For cover in the US enquire with The American Horse Shows Association.

In general, insurance premiums increase with the number of options required. However, permanent incapacity and veterinary fee options are always the most expensive. They are often worth paying for.

54 A freeze mark is a permanent means of identification

It is a good idea to ask your veterinary surgeon to recommend an insurance company as he will have experience as to which of them are prompt and fair in paying claims, and which are not. Also, owners should obtain quotes from several companies and read the small print before making a decision. The most inexpensive policies are not always the best.

Options for cover

Some insurance policies allow horse owners to choose which options they need to suit their individual requirements, while others have blanket policies covering a number of options, some of which the owner may not require.

Options offered include:
- Death from accident or illness (necessitating humane destruction by a veterinary surgeon). This includes loss during foaling and transportation. Humane destruction does not apply to horses who are not suffering but are unable to carry out the work being asked of them. Unless euthanasia is carried out as an emergency to prevent future pain and suffering the permission from the insurance company is required before the horse can be destroyed.
- Loss by theft or straying, including recovery fees up to a specified amount.
- Hire of a replacement animal after theft.
- Veterinary fees caused by accidental injury or illness (usually omitting foaling and vaccinations). This is a worthwhile option but often the policies vary considerably in the amount of cover provided, so search around for the best offer.
- Permanent incapacity caused by accident, sickness or disease. This is the permanent loss of use option, and means that the insurance company will provide cover should the horse be rendered permanently incapable of fulfilling the requirements for which it was purchased. This usually excludes blemishes on show horses.
- Third party legal liability.
- Loss of entry fees.
- Insurance of tack and saddlery.
- Stable expenses.
- Accidental bodily injury causing death or permanent injuries to the rider.
- Dental treatment.

INDEX